VECTORS

Supplement

THOMSON

NELSON

Australia   Canada   Mexico   Singapore   Spain   United Kingdom   United States

THOMSON

NELSON

Vectors 12 Supplement

General Manager, Mathematics, Science, and Technology
Lenore Brooks

Publisher, Mathematics
Colin Garnham

Associate Publisher, Mathematics
Sandra McTavish

Managing Editor, Development
David Spiegel

Product Manager
Linda Krepinsky

Developmental Editor
David Gargaro

Editorial Assistant
Caroline Winter

Executive Director, Content and Media Production
Renate McCloy

Director, Content and Media Production
Linh Vu

Content Production Editor
Jennifer Lee

Production Manager
Cathy Deak

Senior Production Coordinator
Sharon Latta Paterson

Design Director
Ken Phipps

Cover Design
Eugene Lo

Cover Image
Enrique Sallent/ShutterStock

Director, Asset Management Services
Vicki Gould

Photo/Permissions Researcher
Bhisham Kinha

Photo Credits
Chapter 1
1: Jim Larson/ShutterStock
4:Répási Lajos Attila/ShutterStock

Chapter 2
41: Cristina Ferrari/ShutterStock
42:MaxFX/ShutterStock

Chapter 3
83: Enrique Sallent/ShutterStock
85:Agb/ShutterStock

Chapter 4
119: Miroslav Tolimir/ShutterStock
121: iofoto/ShutterStock

Printer
Webcom Limited

Contents

CHAPTER 4
Equations of Planes   119

VECTORS

Have you ever tried to swim across a river with a strong current? Have you sailed a boat, or run into a head wind? If your answer is yes, then you have experienced the effect of vector quantities. Vectors were developed in the middle of the nineteenth century as mathematical tools for studying physics. In the following century, vectors became an essential tool of navigators, engineers, and physicists. In order to navigate, pilots need to know what effect a crosswind will have on the direction in which they intend to fly. In order to build bridges, engineers need to know what load a particular design will support. Physicists use vectors in determining the thrust required to move a space shuttle in a certain direction. You will learn more about vectors in this chapter, and how vectors represent quantities possessing both magnitude and direction.

CHAPTER EXPECTATIONS In this chapter, you will

- represent vectors as directed line segments, **Section 1.1**
- determine the components and projection of a geometric vector, **Section 1.1**
- perform mathematical operations on geometric vectors, **Section 1.2**
- model and solve problems involving velocity and force, **Section 1.3, 1.4**

Review of Prerequisite Skills

A **vector** is a quantity, an inseparable part of which is a direction. Pause for a moment and think about physical quantities that have a direction. Force is an example. The force of gravity acts only downward, never sideways. Wind is another example. A wind from the north and a wind from the south have different physical consequences, even if the wind speeds are the same. Temperature, on the other hand, is not a vector quantity. Temperature does not *go* in any direction. Temperature is referred to as a **scalar** quantity.

We need both scalar and vector quantities to model complex physical systems. Meteorologists, for example, need data on air temperature and wind velocity, among other things, to make weather forecasts.

The object of this chapter is to introduce the mathematical properties of vectors and then show how vectors and scalars are used to describe many features of the physical world.

In this chapter, we introduce the concept of a vector, a mathematical object representing a physical quantity that has both magnitude and direction. We will concentrate on geometric representations of vectors, so that most of our discussion will be of two-dimensional vectors. In later chapters we will introduce algebraic representations of vectors, which will be more easily extended to higher dimensions.

Before we begin this chapter, we will review some basic facts of trigonometry.

TRIGONOMETRIC RATIOS

In a right-angled triangle, as shown,

$$\sin \theta = \frac{a}{c} \qquad \cos \theta = \frac{b}{c}$$
$$\tan \theta = \frac{a}{b}$$

Note: The ratios depend on which angle is θ and which angle is $90°$.

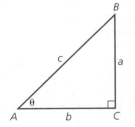

THE SINE LAW

$$\frac{a}{\sin A} = \frac{b}{\sin B} = \frac{c}{\sin C}$$

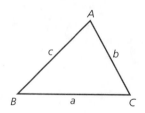

THE COSINE LAW

$$a^2 = b^2 + c^2 - 2bc \cos A \text{ or } \cos A = \frac{b^2 + c^2 - a^2}{2bc}$$

Exercise

1. State the exact value of each of the following.

   a. sin 60°　　　　　　b. cos 60°　　　　　　c. sin 135°

   d. tan 120°　　　　　　e. cos 30°　　　　　　f. tan 45°

2. A triangle ABC has $AB = 6$, $\angle B = 90°$, and $AC = 10$. State the exact value of $\tan A$.

3. In $\triangle XYZ$, $XY = 6$, $\angle X = 60°$, and $\angle Y = 70°$. Determine the values of XZ, YZ, and $\angle Z$ to two-decimal accuracy.

4. In $\triangle PQR$, $PQ = 4$, $PR = 7$, and $QR = 5$. Determine the measures of the angles to the nearest degree.

5. An aircraft control tower T is tracking two planes at points A, 3.5 km from T, and B, 6 km from T. If $\angle ATB = 70°$, determine the distance between the planes.

6. Three ships are at points A, B, and C such that $AB = 2$ km, $AC = 7$ km, and $\angle BAC = 142°$. What is the distance between B and C?

Neuroscientists have found cells in a deep layer of a part of the brain called the superior colliculus. These cells are tuned to the directions of distant visual and auditory stimuli. Each cell responds only to stimuli from a specific direction. Different cells are tuned to different directions. The tuning is broad, and the regions to which different cells are tuned overlap considerably. Neuroscientists have asked what it is about the activity in a group of cells with overlapping tuning regions that specifies the actual direction of a stimulus. For example, how is it that we can point accurately in the direction of a distant sound without seeing its source? One answer is that a cell responds more vigorously when the distance stimulus is in its direction. The direction is determined not by which cell fires most vigorously, but by a type of addition of the degrees to which the various cells have responded to the stimulus.

Investigate and Inquire

The type of addition performed in the brain can be illustrated by a simple case involving only two brain cells. Suppose that one of these cells responds to stimuli that are approximately north, while the other responds to stimuli that are approximately east. If the north cell responds twice as vigorously as the east cell, what is the direction of the stimulus? We can use vector addition to find out.

The answer is found by forming a triangle with a side pointing east and a side pointing north. The side pointing north is twice as long as the side pointing east. The third side is the actual direction of the stimulus. From the diagram, we see $\tan \theta = \frac{1}{2}$. Solving, we find

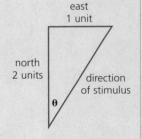

$\theta = \tan^{-1} \left(\frac{1}{2} \right) \cong 26.6°$.

So $\theta = 26.6°$.

Thus, the stimulus is 26.6° east of north.

What direction would be represented by a northeast cell responding three times as vigorously as an east cell?

DISCUSSION QUESTIONS

1. How many cells would be needed to represent all the directions in the plane?

2. Why do you think the direction is not just taken to be the one corresponding to the cell that fires most vigorously? ●

Section 1.1 — Vector Concepts

Vectors are a part of everyone's common experience. Consider a typical winter weather report that you might hear on the nightly news: *The temperature is presently –11 °C, with wind from the northwest at 22 km/h.* This weather report contains two different types of quantities. One quantity (the temperature) is expressed as a single numerical value. The other quantity (the wind velocity) has a numerical value (its magnitude) and also a direction associated with it.

These quantities are typical of the kinds encountered in science. They are classified as follows:

> Quantities having magnitude only are called **scalars**.
> Quantities having both magnitude and direction are called **vectors**.

There seems to be some overlap here. For example, the temperature could be thought of as having magnitude (11°) and direction (negative); in that sense, it could be considered as a one-dimensional vector. There is no problem with this interpretation; sometimes it is a useful way to look at such quantities. However, in most situations we find it easier to use positive and negative numbers as scalars, and restrict the term *vectors* to quantities that require (at least) two properties to define them.

Some examples of vector quantities are:

Force The force of gravity has a well defined magnitude and acts in a specific direction (down). The force of gravity is measured when you step on a scale. Force is a vector quantity.

Displacement When you walk from point A to point B, you travel a certain distance in a certain direction. Displacement is a vector quantity.

Magnetic Field Some magnets are strong; others are weak. All cause a compass needle to swing around and point in a particular direction. A magnetic field is a vector quantity.

In a diagram, a vector is represented by an arrow: ↗. The length of the arrow is a positive real number and represents the magnitude of the vector. The direction in which the arrow points is the direction of the vector. For now we will restrict our discussion to vectors in two dimensions or to situations that can be expressed in two dimensions. Our definitions and conclusions are easily extended to three dimensions (or more).

EXAMPLE 1

A student travels to school by bus, first riding 2 km west, then changing buses and riding a further 3 km north. Represent these displacements on a vector diagram.

Solution

Suppose you represent a 1-km distance by a 1-cm line segment. Then, a 2-cm arrow pointing left represents the first leg of the bus trip. A 3-cm arrow pointing up represents the second leg. The total trip is represented by a diagram combining these vectors.

The notation used to describe vector quantities is as follows:

The algebraic symbol used in this text for a vector is a letter with an arrow on top. Some texts use boldface letters for vectors.

$\vec{u}, \vec{v}$ are vectors

$\boldsymbol{u}, \boldsymbol{v}$ are also vectors

Scalar quantities are written as usual.

x, y, a, b are scalars

The magnitude of a vector is expressed by placing the vector symbol in absolute value brackets. The magnitude of a vector is a positive scalar.

$|\vec{u}|, |\vec{v}|$ are the magnitudes of the vectors $\vec{u}, \vec{v}$

Often it is necessary to explicitly state the initial point and the end point of a vector. Then, two capital letters are used. Such vectors are referred to as **point-to-point vectors**.

$\overrightarrow{AB}$ is the vector that starts at point A and ends at point B.

Its magnitude is $|\overrightarrow{AB}|$.

Certain other terms are used in connection with vectors.

Two vectors are *equal* if and only if their magnitudes and their directions are the same.

Two vectors are *opposite* if they have the same magnitude but point in opposite directions.

When two vectors are opposite, such as $\overrightarrow{AB}$ and $\overrightarrow{CD}$, one is the *negative* of the other: $\overrightarrow{AB} = -\overrightarrow{CD}$.

Two vectors are *parallel* if their directions are either the same or opposite.

EXAMPLE 2

ABCDEF is a regular hexagon. Give examples of vectors which are

a. equal

b. parallel but having different magnitudes

c. equal in magnitude but opposite in direction

d. equal in magnitude but not parallel

e. different in both magnitude and direction

Solution

a. $\overrightarrow{AB} = \overrightarrow{ED}$

b. $\overrightarrow{FA} \parallel \overrightarrow{EB}$, but $\left|\overrightarrow{FA}\right| \neq \left|\overrightarrow{EB}\right|$

c. $\left|\overrightarrow{FE}\right| = \left|\overrightarrow{CB}\right|$, but $\overrightarrow{FE} = -\overrightarrow{CB}$

d. $\left|\overrightarrow{ED}\right| = \left|\overrightarrow{DC}\right|$, but $\overrightarrow{ED} \neq \overrightarrow{DC}$

e. $\overrightarrow{FB}, \overrightarrow{DC}$

There are other possible answers.

There is no special symbol for the direction of a vector. To specify the direction of a vector, we state the angle it makes with another vector or with some given direction such as a horizontal or vertical axis or a compass direction.

> The **angle between two vectors** is the angle ($\leq 180°$) formed when the vectors are placed tail to tail; that is, starting at the same point.
>
>

One way to determine the angle between two vectors is to examine geometrical relationships and use trigonometry.

EXAMPLE 3

$OABC$ is a square with sides measuring 6 units. E is the midpoint of BC. Find the angle between the following vectors.

a. $\overrightarrow{OB}$ and $\overrightarrow{OC}$ b. $\overrightarrow{OE}$ and $\overrightarrow{OC}$ c. $\overrightarrow{OB}$ and $\overrightarrow{OE}$

Solution

a. The diagonal of the square bisects $\angle AOC$.
   The angle between $\overrightarrow{OB}$ and $\overrightarrow{OC}$ is 45°.

b. Using trigonometry, $\tan \angle EOC = \frac{3}{6}$, $\angle EOC \cong 26.6°$, so the angle between $\overrightarrow{OE}$ and $\overrightarrow{OC}$ is 26.6°.

c. The angle between $\overrightarrow{OB}$ and $\overrightarrow{OE}$ is the difference $45° - 26.6° = 18.4°$.

When two vectors are parallel, one of the vectors can be expressed in terms of the other using **scalar-multiplication**. Suppose, for example, M is the midpoint of the line segment AB. Since M is the midpoint, then $\left|\overrightarrow{AB}\right| = 2\left|\overrightarrow{AM}\right|$, and since the directions of $\overrightarrow{AB}$ and $\overrightarrow{AM}$ are the same, we write the **vector equations**

$$\overrightarrow{AB} = 2\overrightarrow{AM} \quad \text{or} \quad \overrightarrow{AM} = \tfrac{1}{2}\overrightarrow{AB} \quad \text{or} \quad \overrightarrow{BM} = -\tfrac{1}{2}\overrightarrow{AB}.$$

Thus, multiplication of a vector by a scalar k results in a new vector parallel to the original one but with a different magnitude. It is true in general that two vectors $\vec{u}$ and $\vec{v}$ are parallel if and only if $\vec{u} = k\vec{v}$.

A particularly useful type of vector is a vector with magnitude 1. Such vectors are called **unit vectors**. A unit vector is denoted by a *carat* (^) placed over the symbol. When a vector and a unit vector are denoted by the same letter, for example $\vec{v}$ and $\hat{v}$, you should understand $\hat{v}$ to be a unit vector having the same direction as $\vec{v}$. Any vector can be expressed as a scalar multiple of a unit vector.

Unit Vectors

1. A unit vector in the direction of any vector $\vec{v}$ can be found by dividing $\vec{v}$ by its magnitude $\left|\vec{v}\right|$:
$$\hat{v} = \frac{1}{\left|\vec{v}\right|}\vec{v}$$

2. Any vector $\vec{v}$ can be expressed as the product of its magnitude $\left|\vec{v}\right|$ and a unit vector $\hat{v}$ in the direction of $\vec{v}$:
$$\vec{v} = \left|\vec{v}\right|\hat{v}$$

Another useful type of vector has magnitude 0. Such vectors are valuable even though their direction is undefined. The **zero vector** is denoted by $\vec{0}$.

EXAMPLE 4

Examine the vectors in the diagram.

a. Express $\vec{b}$ and $\vec{c}$ each as a scalar multiple of $\vec{a}$.

b. Express $\vec{a}$, $\vec{b}$, and $\vec{c}$ each in terms of the unit vector $\hat{a}$.

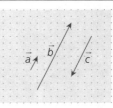

Solution

a. On the grid, each vector lies on the hypotenuse of a right-angled triangle with sides in the ratio 1:2, so the three vectors are parallel. The magnitudes of $\vec{a}$, $\vec{b}$, and $\vec{c}$ can be found using the Pythagorean Theorem.

$$\left|\vec{a}\right| = \sqrt{1^2 + 2^2} = \sqrt{5}, \ \left|\vec{b}\right| = \sqrt{5^2 + 10^2} = 5\sqrt{5},$$
and $\left|\vec{c}\right| = \sqrt{3^2 + 6^2} = 3\sqrt{5}$

Therefore $\vec{b} = 5\vec{a}$ and $\vec{c} = -3\vec{a}$.

b. The unit vector in the direction of $\vec{a}$ is $\hat{a} = \dfrac{1}{\sqrt{5}}\vec{a}$. Then $\vec{a} = \sqrt{5}\hat{a}$, $\vec{b} = 5\sqrt{5}\hat{a}$, and $\vec{c} = -3\sqrt{5}\hat{a}$.

Exercise 1.1

Part A

1. In your own words, explain the difference between a scalar and a vector.

2. Which of these physical quantities is a vector and which is a scalar?
    a. the acceleration of a drag racer
    b. the mass of the moon
    c. the velocity of a wave at a beach
    d. the frequency of a musical note
    e. the speed of light
    f. the age of a child
    g. the friction on an ice surface
    h. the volume of a box
    i. the energy produced by an electric generator
    j. the force of gravity
    k. the speedometer reading in an automobile
    l. the momentum of a curling stone
    m. the time on a kitchen clock
    n. the magnetic field of the earth
    o. the density of a lead weight
    p. the pressure of the atmosphere
    q. the area of a parallelogram
    r. the temperature of a swimming pool

3. For each part of Example 2, state a second answer.

Part B

4. One car travelling 75 km/h passes another going 50 km/h. Draw vectors that represent the velocities of the two cars if they are going
    a. in the same direction
    b. in opposite directions

5. What is the angle between the following directions?
    a. *N* and *NE*
    b. *E* and *SW*
    c. *S* and *W*

6. Draw a vector to represent
    a. the velocity of a fishing boat travelling at 8 knots on a heading of *S* 75° *W* (A knot is a speed of one nautical mile per hour.)
    b. the position of a city intersection 7 blocks east and 3 blocks south of your present position
    c. the displacement of a crate that moves 6 m up a conveyor belt inclined at an angle of 18°
    d. the force exerted by a chain hoist carrying a load of 200 kg

7. Radar in the control tower of an airport shows aircraft at directions of $N\ 50°\ E$, $N\ 70°\ W$, and $S\ 20°\ W$, and distances of 5, 8, and 12 km, respectively.

   a. In a diagram, draw vectors showing the positon of the three aircraft in relation to the tower.

   b. The aircraft are travelling at velocities of 450 kph N, 550 kph $N\ 70°\ W$, and 175 kph $N\ 20°\ E$, respectively. At the positon of each aircraft in part **a**, draw small vectors to represent their velocities.

8. The points A, B, C, D, E, F, and G are equally spaced along a line. Name a vector which is equal to

   a. $3\overrightarrow{BD}$ b. $\frac{1}{4}\overrightarrow{EA}$ c. $\frac{5}{2}\overrightarrow{DF}$ d. $\frac{2}{3}\overrightarrow{GC}$ e. $-2\overrightarrow{AD}$

9. $ABCD$ is a rhombus. For each of the following, find two vectors $\vec{u}$ and $\vec{v}$ in this diagram (expressed as point-to-point vectors) such that

   a. $\vec{u} = \vec{v}$ b. $\vec{u} = -\vec{v}$

   c. $\vec{u} = 2\vec{v}$ d. $\vec{u} = \frac{1}{2}\vec{v}$

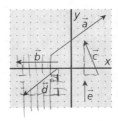

10. During takeoff, an aircraft rises 100 m for every 520 m of horizontal motion. Determine the direction of its velocity.

11. Determine the magnitude and the direction of each of the vectors in the given diagram. Express each direction as an angle measured counter-clockwise from a unit vector in the positive x direction.

12. A search and rescue aircraft, travelling at a speed of 240 km/h, starts out at a heading of $N\ 20°\ W$. After travelling for 1 h 15 min, it turns to a heading of $N\ 80°\ E$ and continues for another 2 hours before returning to base.

    a. Determine the displacement vector for each leg of the trip.

    b. Find the total distance the aircraft travelled and how long it took.

Part C

13. For what values of k is $|(k - 2)\vec{v}| < |4\vec{v}|$, $(\vec{v} \neq \vec{0})$?

14. Prove that two vectors $\vec{u}$ and $\vec{v}$ are parallel if and only if $\vec{u} = k\vec{v}$.

In many applications of vectors to physical problems, we must find the combined effect or *sum* of two or more vectors. What, for example, is the combined effect of two or more forces acting on an object? How does wind velocity affect the velocity of an aircraft?

To determine the sum of two vectors, let us look first for a geometrical answer. Suppose the rectangle $ABCD$ is a park at the corner of an intersection. To get from A to C, some people will walk along the sidewalk from A to B and then from B to C. They follow a route described by the sum of two displacement vectors: $\overrightarrow{AB} + \overrightarrow{BC}$. Others may follow a shortcut through the park directly from A to C. This route is described by the displacement vector $\overrightarrow{AC}$.

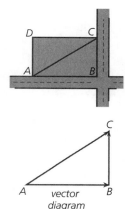

Whichever route is followed, the displacement is the same; both get from A to C. Therefore, $\overrightarrow{AB} + \overrightarrow{BC} = \overrightarrow{AC}$.

vector diagram

This model for vector addition is valid for all vectors because, in general, vectors can be represented geometrically by a directed line segment.

Triangle Law of Vector Addition

To find the sum of two vectors $\vec{u}$ and $\vec{v}$ using the triangle law of vector addition, draw the two vectors head to tail. The sum $\vec{u} + \vec{v}$, or *resultant*, is the vector from the tail of the first to the head of the second.

The order in which we add the vectors is unimportant. If the vectors are added in the opposite order, the result is the same. This demonstrates that vectors satisfy the **commutative law of addition:** $\vec{u} + \vec{v} = \vec{v} + \vec{u}$.

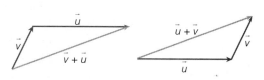

By combining the two triangles of the triangle law in one diagram, a parallelogram is formed.

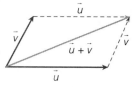

Parallelogram Law of Vector Addition
>
> To find the sum of two vectors using the parallelogram law of vector addition, draw the two vectors tail to tail. Complete the parallelogram with these vectors as sides. The sum $\vec{u} + \vec{v}$ is the diagonal of the parallelogram from the point where the tails are joined to the point where the heads meet.

These two laws of addition are equivalent. The method we use depends on which is the most convenient for the problem at hand. When you set out to solve a problem involving vectors, start by drawing vector diagrams such as those on page 11.

EXAMPLE 1

Given the three vectors $\vec{a}$, $\vec{b}$, and $\vec{c}$, sketch the sums $\vec{a} + \vec{b}$ and $(\vec{a} + \vec{b}) + \vec{c}$, $\vec{b} + \vec{c}$, $\vec{a} + (\vec{b} + \vec{c})$.

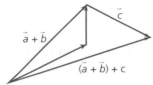

Solution

Adding $\vec{a}$ to $\vec{b}$ first, we obtain

Adding $\vec{b}$ to $\vec{c}$ first, we obtain

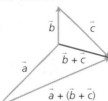

This example illustrates that vectors satisfy the *associative law of addition*: $\vec{a} + (\vec{b} + \vec{c}) = (\vec{a} + \vec{b}) + \vec{c}$. It means that we can omit the brackets and write simply $\vec{a} + \vec{b} + \vec{c}$.

EXAMPLE 2

Find the magnitude and direction of the sum of two vectors $\vec{u}$ and $\vec{v}$, if their magnitudes are 5 and 8 units, respectively, and the angle between them is 30°.

Solution

Make a vector diagram showing the two vectors with an angle of 30° between them. Complete the parallelogram and draw the resultant.

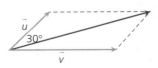

The resultant is the third side of a triangle with sides 5 and 8. Observe that the angle between the vectors is *not* an angle in this triangle. The angle between the vectors is equal to an exterior angle of the triangle. (Why?) Use the angle of 150° and the cosine law to find the magnitude of the sum.

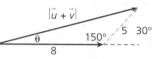

$$|\vec{u} + \vec{v}|^2 = 5^2 + 8^2 - 2(5)(8) \cos 150°$$
$$= 158.28$$

Then $|\vec{u} + \vec{v}| \cong 12.6$

The direction of $\vec{u} + \vec{v}$ is expressed as an angle measured relative to one of the given vectors, say $\vec{v}$. This is θ in the diagram. It can be found using the sine law.

$$\frac{\sin \theta}{5} = \frac{\sin 150°}{12.6}$$

$$\sin \theta = \frac{5 \sin 150°}{12.6}$$

$$\theta \cong 11.4°$$

Therefore, the magnitude of $\vec{u} + \vec{v}$ is 12.6 units, and it makes an angle of approximately 11.4° with $\vec{v}$.

To subtract two vectors $\vec{a}$ and $\vec{b}$, we express the difference in terms of a sum. To find the vector $\vec{a} - \vec{b}$, use the opposite of $\vec{b}$ and add it to $\vec{a}$. Hence $\vec{a} - \vec{b}$ is equivalent to $\vec{a} + (-\vec{b})$.

The difference of two equal vectors $\vec{a} - \vec{a}$ is the **zero vector**, denoted by $\vec{0}$. The zero vector has zero magnitude. Its direction is indeterminate.

EXAMPLE 3

In parallelogram $ABCD$, find the difference $\overrightarrow{AB} - \overrightarrow{AD}$

    a. geometrically   b. algebraically

Solution

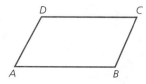

a. Draw $\overrightarrow{AD'}$ opposite to $\overrightarrow{AD}$. Using the parallelogram law, draw the sum $\overrightarrow{AB} + \overrightarrow{AD'}$, which is $\overrightarrow{AC'}$ in the diagram.

But $\overrightarrow{AC'} = \overrightarrow{DB}$, so $\overrightarrow{AB} - \overrightarrow{AD} = \overrightarrow{DB}$

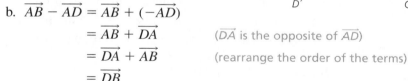

b. $\overrightarrow{AB} - \overrightarrow{AD} = \overrightarrow{AB} + (-\overrightarrow{AD})$
$$= \overrightarrow{AB} + \overrightarrow{DA} \qquad (\overrightarrow{DA} \text{ is the opposite of } \overrightarrow{AD})$$
$$= \overrightarrow{DA} + \overrightarrow{AB} \qquad (\text{rearrange the order of the terms})$$
$$= \overrightarrow{DB}$$

In the parallelogram formed by two vectors $\vec{u}$ and $\vec{v}$

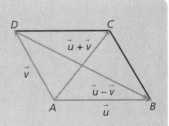

- the sum $\vec{u} + \vec{v}$ is the vector created by the diagonal from the tail of the two vectors
  $$\vec{u} + \vec{v} = \overrightarrow{AC}$$

- the difference $\vec{u} - \vec{v}$ is the vector created by the second diagonal
  $$\vec{u} - \vec{v} = \overrightarrow{DB}$$

Properties of Vector Addition
- $\vec{a} + \vec{b} = \vec{b} + \vec{a}$ Commutative Law
- $(\vec{a} + \vec{b}) + \vec{c} = \vec{a} + (\vec{b} + \vec{c})$ Associative Law

Properties of Scalar Multiplication
- $(mn)\vec{a} = m(n\vec{a})$ Associative Law
- $m(\vec{a} + \vec{b}) = m\vec{a} + m\vec{b}$ Distributive Laws
- $(m+n)\vec{a} = m\vec{a} + n\vec{a}$

Properties of the Zero Vector: $\vec{0}$
- $\vec{a} + \vec{0} = \vec{a}$

Each vector $\vec{a}$ has a negative $(-\vec{a})$ such that
$\vec{a} + (-\vec{a}) = \vec{0}$.

These laws state that you may add vectors in any order you like and that you may expand and factor expressions in the usual way.

There are other basic vector relations that are universally true. We can demonstrate the validity of these relations by using vector diagrams. The following example illustrates this.

EXAMPLE 4

Show that $|\vec{u} + \vec{v}| \leq |\vec{u}| + |\vec{v}|$. When does equality hold?

Solution

Make a diagram of two vectors $\vec{u}$ and $\vec{v}$, and their sum $\vec{u} + \vec{v}$. The three vectors form a triangle. The lengths of the sides of the triangle are the magnitudes of the vectors. From the diagram, the side $|\vec{u} + \vec{v}|$ must be less than the sum of the other two sides $|\vec{u}| + |\vec{v}|$. There is no triangle if it is greater.

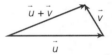

Therefore, $|\vec{u} + \vec{v}| < |\vec{u}| + |\vec{v}|$.

When $\vec{u}$ and $\vec{v}$ have the same direction, the triangle collapses to a single line, and $|\vec{u} + \vec{v}| = |\vec{u}| + |\vec{v}|$.

Triangle Inequality
For vectors $\vec{u}$ and $\vec{v}$, $|\vec{u} + \vec{v}| \leq |\vec{u}| + |\vec{v}|$.

Exercise 1.2

Part A

1. For each of the following, state the name of a vector equal to $\vec{u} + \vec{v}$ and equal to $\vec{u} - \vec{v}$.

a.

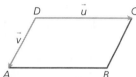

b.

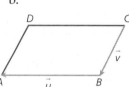

c.

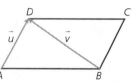

2. Seven points A, B, C, D, E, F, and G, are arranged in order from left to right on a single straight line. Express the vector $\vec{BE}$ as

a. the sum of two vectors, three vectors, and four vectors

b. the difference of two vectors in two different ways

3. What single vector is equivalent to each of these sums?

a. $\vec{PT} + \vec{TS} + \vec{SQ}$

b. $\vec{AC} - \vec{GE} + \vec{CE}$

c. $\vec{EA} - \vec{CB} + \vec{DB} + \vec{AD}$

d. $\vec{PT} - \vec{QT} + \vec{SR} - \vec{SQ}$

Part B

4. Find the sum of the vectors $\vec{u}$ and $\vec{v}$ if θ is the angle between them.

a. $|\vec{u}| = 12$, $|\vec{v}| = 21$, and $\theta = 70°$ b. $|\vec{u}| = 3$, $|\vec{v}| = 10$, and $\theta = 115°$

5. A tour boat travels 25 km due east and then 15 km $S\ 50°\ E$. Represent these displacements in a vector diagram, then calculate the resultant displacement.

6. If $\hat{a}$ and $\hat{b}$ are unit vectors that make an angle of 60° with each other, calculate

a. $|3\hat{a} - 5\hat{b}|$

b. $|8\hat{a} + 3\hat{b}|$

7. What conditions must be satisfied by the vectors $\vec{u}$ and $\vec{v}$ for the following to be true?

a. $|\vec{u} + \vec{v}| = |\vec{u} - \vec{v}|$ b. $|\vec{u} + \vec{v}| > |\vec{u} - \vec{v}|$ c. $|\vec{u} + \vec{v}| < |\vec{u} - \vec{v}|$

8. Under what conditions will three vectors having magnitudes of 7, 24, and 25, respectively, have the zero vector as a resultant?

9. Vectors $\vec{a}$ and $\vec{b}$ have magnitudes 2 and 3, respectively. If the angle between them is 50°, find the vector $5\vec{a} - 2\vec{b}$, and state its magnitude and direction.

10. Simplify the following expressions using the properties of vector operations.

a. $4\vec{x} - 5\vec{y} - \vec{x} + 6\vec{y}$ b. $2\vec{x} - 4(\vec{x} - \vec{y})$

c. $8(3\vec{x} + 5\vec{y}) - 4(6\vec{x} - 9\vec{y})$ d. $3\vec{x} - 6\vec{y} + 4(2\vec{y} - \vec{x}) - 6\vec{x}$

11. Let $\vec{a} = 2\vec{i} - 3\vec{j} + \vec{k}$, $\vec{b} = \vec{i} + \vec{j} + \vec{k}$, and $\vec{c} = 2\vec{i} - 3\vec{k}$. Find

a. $\vec{a} + \vec{b} + \vec{c}$ b. $\vec{a} + 2\vec{b} - 3\vec{c}$ c. $-3\vec{b} + 4\vec{c}$

12. If $\vec{a} = 3\vec{x} + 2\vec{y}$ and $\vec{b} = 5\vec{x} - 4\vec{y}$, find $\vec{x}$ and $\vec{y}$ in terms of $\vec{a}$ and $\vec{b}$.

13. Check each identity algebraically, and illustrate with the use of a diagram.

a. $\vec{x} + \dfrac{\vec{y} - \vec{x}}{2} = \dfrac{\vec{x} + \vec{y}}{2}$ b. $\vec{x} - \dfrac{\vec{x} + \vec{y}}{2} = \dfrac{\vec{x} - \vec{y}}{2}$

14. Illustrate for $k > 0$ that $k(\vec{u} + \vec{v}) = k\vec{u} + k\vec{v}$.

15. Show geometrically that, for any scalar k and any vectors $\vec{u}$ and $\vec{v}$,
$k(\vec{u} - \vec{v}) = k\vec{u} - k\vec{v}$.

16. By considering the angles between the vectors, show that $\vec{a} + \vec{b}$ and $\vec{a} - \vec{b}$ are perpendicular when $|\vec{a}| = |\vec{b}|$.

Part C

17. *ABCDEF* is a regular hexagon with sides of unit length. Find the magnitude and the direction of $\overrightarrow{AB} + \overrightarrow{AC} + \overrightarrow{AD} + \overrightarrow{AE} + \overrightarrow{AF}$.

18. If $|\vec{x}| = 11$, $|\vec{y}| = 23$, and $|\vec{x} - \vec{y}| = 30$, find $|\vec{x} + \vec{y}|$.

19. The sum and the difference of two vectors $\vec{u}$ and $\vec{v}$ are given. Show how to find the vectors themselves.

20. Represent by $\hat{i}, \hat{j}$, and $\hat{k}$ the three vectors $\overrightarrow{AB}, \overrightarrow{AC}$, and $\overrightarrow{AD}$ that lie along adjacent edges of the cube in the given diagram. Express each of the following vectors in terms of $\hat{i}, \hat{j}$, and $\hat{k}$.

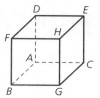

   a. $\overrightarrow{FG}$, a diagonal of the front face of the cube

   b. the other diagonals of the front, top, and right faces of the cube

   c. $\overrightarrow{BE}$, a body diagonal of the cube

   d. the other body diagonals of the cube

   e. What is the magnitude of a face diagonal? A body diagonal?

21. Prove that for any vectors $\vec{u}$ and $\vec{v}$, $|\vec{u} + \vec{v}|^2 + |\vec{u} - \vec{v}|^2 = 2(|\vec{u}|^2 + |\vec{v}|^2)$.

Section 1.3 — Force as a Vector

A force on any object causes that object to undergo an acceleration. You can feel a force pushing you back into your seat whenever the car you are riding in accelerates from a stop light. You no longer feel any force once the car has reached a steady speed, but that does not mean that the force that set the car in motion has ceased to exist. Instead that force is now balanced by other forces such as air resistance and road friction. A steady speed is an example of a **state of equilibrium** in which the net force is zero.

It was Newton who first clarified these concepts and formulated the law that bears his name.

> **Newton's First Law of Motion**
> An object will remain in a state of equilibrium (which is a state of rest or a state of uniform motion) unless it is compelled to change that state by the action of an outside force.

The outside force mentioned in Newton's First Law refers to an unbalanced force. When you release a helium-filled balloon, it will rise into the air. It is attracted by the force of gravity like everything else but upward forces are greater, so it accelerates into the sky. Eventually it reaches an altitude where the atmosphere is less dense, and the buoyant forces and the force of gravity balance. In this state of equilibrium, it can float for days, as weather balloons often do.

EXAMPLE 1

Describe the forces acting on an aircraft flying at constant velocity.

Solution

An aircraft flying at a constant velocity is in a state of equilibrium. The engines provide thrust, the force propelling the aircraft forward. The thrust is counterbalanced by a drag force coming from air resistance. The air rushing past the wings produces lift, a force which counterbalances the force of gravity and keeps the plane aloft.

lift

drag ← *aircraft* → *thrust*

weight

The magnitude of a force is measured in newtons, which is abbreviated as N. At the earth's surface, gravity causes objects to accelerate at a rate of approximately 9.8 m/s^2 as they fall. The magnitude of the gravitational force is the product of an object's mass and this acceleration. The gravitational force on a 1-kg object at the earth's surface is approximately 9.8 N. In other words, a 1-kg object weighs approximately 9.8 N.

It is generally the case that several forces act on an object at once. It is important to know the net effect of all these forces because an object's state of motion is determined by this net force. Since forces are vectors, the single force that has the same effect as all the forces acting together can be found by vector addition. This single force is the *resultant* of all the forces.

Sometimes a force acts on an object at an angle, so that only part of the force is affecting the motion of the object.

EXAMPLE 2

Jake is towing his friend on a toboggan, using a rope which makes an angle of 25° with the ground. If Jake is pulling with a force of 70 N, what horizontal force is he exerting on the toboggan?

Solution

First draw a diagram showing the force and its direction. Now consider that this force is the resultant of a horizontal force $\vec{h}$ and a vertical force $\vec{v}$. We show this by forming a triangle, with the original 70 N force as the resultant; $\vec{h}$ and $\vec{v}$ are perpendicular.

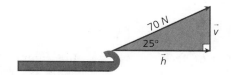

$$\text{Now } |\vec{h}| = 70 \cos 25°$$
$$\cong 63.4$$

So the horizontal force is about 63.4 N.

We refer to the quantieties $|\vec{h}|$ and $|\vec{v}|$ as the horizontal and vertical components of the original force.

EXAMPLE 3

Jake and Maria are towing their friends on a toboggan. Each is exerting a horizontal force of 60 N. Since they are walking side by side, the ropes pull one to each side; they each make an angle of 20° with the line of motion. Find the force pulling the toboggan forward.

Solution

Make a diagram showing the forces. By completing the parallelogram, we show the resultant $\vec{r}$, the diagonal of the parallelogram.

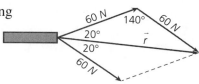

$$|\vec{r}|^2 = 60^2 + 60^2 - 2(60)(60) \cos 140°$$
$$|\vec{r}| \cong 112.8$$

The towing force is about 113 N.

1. We could have solved this question by finding the component of each force along the direction of travel and adding the results.
2. If the forces had not been equal, the angles made with the direction of travel would not have been equal.

In Example 3, the toboggan is (probably) travelling at a constant speed, indicating that there is no unbalanced force on it. This is because there is a frictional force that is equal and opposite to the towing force.

The force that is equal in magnitude but opposite in direction to the resultant is called the **equilibrant**. It exactly counterbalances the resultant. In Example 2, the force of friction is the equilibrant, which keeps the towing force from accelerating the toboggan.

EXAMPLE 4

In Example 2, what if Maria starts pulling at an angle of 30° instead of 20°? As the diagram shows, the direction of the resultant will be a little to the right of the axis of the toboggan. This means that the toboggan will not travel forward in a straight line but will veer continually to the right. If these conditions remain unchanged, the toboggan will travel in a circle.

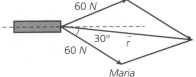

EXAMPLE 5

In Example 2, if Maria pulls with a force of 60 N at an angle of 30°, what should the magnitude of the force exerted by Jake at an angle of 20° be if the toboggan is to move straight forward without turning? According to the sine law,

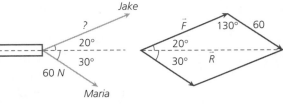

$$\frac{\sin 30°}{|\vec{F}|} = \frac{\sin 20°}{60}$$
$$|\vec{F}| \cong 88 \text{ N}$$

Jake must pull with a force of 88 N. Since Jake is pulling harder than before, the resultant will be greater than before:

$$\frac{\sin 130°}{R} = \frac{\sin 20°}{60}$$
$$R \cong 134 \text{ N}$$

As in Example 2 and the subsequent discussion, make it a practice with force problems to look for ways to justify your numerical results and make them physically meaningful.

EXAMPLE 6

A large promotional balloon is tethered to the top of a building by two guy wires attached at points 20 m apart. If the buoyant force on the balloon is 850 N, and the two guy wires make angles of 58° and 66° with the horizontal, find the tension in each of the wires.

Solution

First draw the position diagram showing where the forces act. In this problem, the resultant of the two tensions must be 850 N to counterbalance the buoyant force of the balloon, which is the equilibrant. In making the force diagram, draw the tension vectors parallel to the corresponding lines in the position diagram.

In the diagrams, observe step by step how the angles in the position diagram are first translated into the force diagram, and then how these angles are used to determine the angles inside the force triangle.

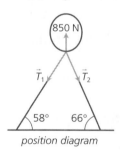

position diagram

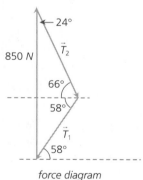

force diagram

Since all three angles in the force triangle are known, the magnitudes of the tension vectors $\vec{T}_1$ and $\vec{T}_2$ can be calculated using the sine law,

$$\frac{|\vec{T}_1|}{\sin 24°} = \frac{850}{\sin 124°} \quad \text{and} \quad \frac{|\vec{T}_2|}{\sin 32°} = \frac{850}{\sin 124°}.$$

Therefore, $\quad |\vec{T}_1| = \dfrac{850 \sin 24°}{\sin 124°} \quad$ and $\quad |\vec{T}_2| = \dfrac{850 \sin 32°}{\sin 124°}$

$$\cong 417 \text{ N} \qquad\qquad\qquad \cong 543 \text{ N}$$

The tensions in the guy wires are approximately 417 N and 543 N, with the guy wire at the steeper angle having the greater tension.

EXAMPLE 7

Is it possible for an object to be in a state of equilibrium when forces of 10 N, 20 N, and 40 N act on it?

Solution
An object will be in a state of equilibrium when the resultant of all the forces acting on it is zero. This means that the three given force vectors must form a triangle. By the triangle inequality theorem, the sum of any two sides must be greater than the third, but in this case the magnitudes of the forces are such that $10 + 20 < 40$. Therefore, an object cannot be in a state of equilibrium with the three given forces acting on it.

In the discussion of forces in the previous examples, we assumed that an object is free to move in the direction of the force acting on it. Often, however, that is not the case. For example, when you push a lawn mower, you exert a force along the handle, but the mower does not move into the ground along the line of the force. It moves horizontally. So, how much of the force that you exert actually contributes to the motion?

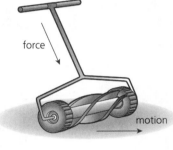

To answer this question, we must resolve the force into horizontal and vertical components. The components are the magnitudes of forces acting horizontally and vertically, whose sum, by vector addition, is the original force.

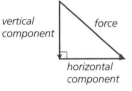

EXAMPLE 8

A lawn mower is pushed with a force of 90 N directed along the handle, which makes an angle of 36° with the ground.

  a. Determine the horizontal and vertical components of the force on the mower.

  b. Describe the physical consequences of each component of the pushing force.

Solution
  a. The force diagram is a right triangle.
    The components are

$$|\vec{F_h}| = 90 \cos 36° \quad \text{and} \quad |\vec{F_v}| = 90 \sin 36°$$
$$\cong 72.8 \text{ N} \qquad\qquad\qquad \cong 52.9 \text{ N}$$

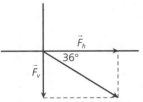

  b. The horizontal component of the force, 72.8 N, moves the lawnmower forward across the grass. The vertical component of the force, 52.9 N, is in the same direction (down) as the force of gravity.

EXAMPLE 9

A 20-kg trunk is resting on a ramp inclined at an angle of 15°. Calculate the components of the force of gravity on the trunk that are parallel and perpendicular to the ramp. Describe the physical consequences of each.

Solution

The force of gravity on the trunk is $(20 \text{ kg}) \times (9.8 \text{ m/s}^2) = 196 \text{ N}$ acting down. The parallel and perpendicular components are

$$|\vec{F}_p| = 196 \sin 15° \quad \text{and} \quad |\vec{F}_n| = 196 \cos 15°$$
$$\cong 51 \text{ N} \qquad\qquad\qquad \cong 189 \text{ N}$$

position diagram

force diagram

The parallel component points down the slope of the ramp. It tends to cause the trunk to slide down the slope. It is opposed by the force of friction acting up the slope. The perpendicular component presses the trunk against the ramp. The magnitude of the force of friction is proportional to this component.

Exercise 1.3

Part A

1. Name some common household objects on which the force of gravity is approximately 2 N; 20 N; 200 N. What is your weight in newtons?

2. Find the horizontal and vertical components of each of the following forces.
   a. 200 N acting at an angle of 30° to the horizontal
   b. 160 N acting at an angle of 71° to the horizontal
   c. 75 N acting at an angle of 51° to the vertical
   d. 36 N acting vertically

3. Find the resultant of each pair of forces acting on an object.
   a. forces of 7 N east and 12 N west
   b. forces of 7 N east and 12 N north
   c. forces of 6 N southwest and 8 N northwest
   d. forces of 6 N southeast and 8 N northwest

Part B

4. Find the magnitude of the resultant of the four forces shown in the given diagram.

5. Two forces $\vec{F}_1$ and $\vec{F}_2$ act at right angles to each other. Express the magnitude and direction of $\vec{F}_1 + \vec{F}_2$ in terms of $|\vec{F}_1|$ and $|\vec{F}_2|$.

6. Find the magnitude and the direction (to the nearest degree) of the resultant of each of the following systems of forces.

   a. forces of 3 N and 8 N acting at an angle of 60° to each other

   b. forces of 15 N and 8 N acting at an angle of 130° to each other

7. Find the magnitude and direction of the equilibrant of each of the following systems of forces.

   a. forces of 32 N and 48 N acting at an angle of 90° to each other

   b. forces of 16 N and 10 N acting at an angle of 10° to each other

8. Is it easier to pull yourself up doing chin-ups when your hands are 60 cm apart or 120 cm apart? Explain your answer.

9. A mass of 10 kg is suspended from a ceiling by two cords that make angles of 30° and 45° with the ceiling. Find the tension in each of the cords.

10. Two forces of equal magnitude act at 60° to each other. If their resultant has a magnitude of 30 N, find the magnitude of the equal forces.

11. Which of the following sets of forces acting on an object could produce equilibrium?

   a. 5 N, 2 N, 13 N

   b. 7 N, 5 N, 5 N

   c. 13 N, 27 N, 14 N

   d. 12 N, 26 N, 13 N

12. Three forces of 5 N, 7 N, and 8 N are applied to an object. If the object is in a state of equilibrium

   a. show how the forces must be arranged

   b. calculate the angle between the lines of action of the 5 N and 7 N forces

13. A man weighing 70 kg lies in a hammock whose ropes make angles of 20° and 25° with the horizontal. What is the tension in each rope?

14. A steel wire 40 m long is suspended between two fixed points 20 m apart. A force of 375 N pulls the wire down at a point 15 m from one end of the wire. State the tension in each part of the wire.

15. An advertising sign is supported by a horizontal steel brace extending at right angles from the side of a building, and by a wire attached to the building above the brace at an angle of 25°. If the force of gravity on the sign is 850 N, find the tension in the wire and the compression in the steel brace.

16. Find the x- and y-components of each of the vectors $\vec{u}$, $\vec{v}$, and $\vec{w}$.

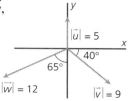

17. A tractor is towing a log using a cable inclined at an angle of 15° to the horizontal. If the tension in the cable is 1470 N, what is the horizontal force moving the log?

18. A piece of luggage is on a conveyer belt that is inclined at an angle of 28°. If the luggage has a mass of 20 kg

   a. determine the components of the force of gravity parallel to and perpendicular to the conveyer belt

   b. explain the physical effect of each of these components

19. A child with a mass of 35 kg is sitting on a swing attached to a tree branch by a rope 5 m in length. The child is pulled back 1.5 m measured horizontally.

   a. What horizontal force will hold the child in this position?

   b. What is the tension in the rope?

20. The main rotor of a helicopter produces a force of 55 kN. If the helicopter flies with the rotor revolving about an axis tilted at an angle of 8° to the vertical

   a. find the components of the rotor force parallel to and perpendicular to the ground

   b. explain the physical effect on the helicopter of each component of the rotor force

21. In order to keep a 250-kg crate from sliding down a ramp inclined at 25°, the force of friction that acts parallel to and up the ramp must have a magnitude of at least how many newtons?

22. A lawn roller with a mass of 50 kg is being pulled with a force of 320 N. If the handle of the roller makes an angle of 42° with the ground, what horizontal component of the force is causing the roller to move?

Part C

23. Three forces, each of which is perpendicular to the other two, act on an object. If the magnitudes of these forces are 6 N, 15 N, and 10 N, respectively, find the magnitude and direction of the resultant. (State the angles that the resultant makes with the two larger forces.)

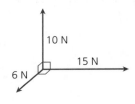

24. Two tugs are towing a ship. The smaller tug is 10° off the port bow and the larger tug is 20° off the starboard bow. The larger tug pulls twice as hard as the smaller tug. In what direction will the ship move?

25. Braided cotton string will break when the tension exceeds 300 N. Suppose that a weight of 400 N is suspended from a 200-cm length of string, the upper ends of which are tied to a horizontal rod at points 120 cm apart.

    a. Show that the string will support the weight, when the weight is hung at the centre of the string.

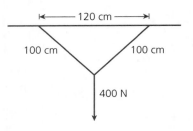

    b. Will the string break if the weight is 80 cm from one end of the string?

In elementary problems, the **speed** of a moving object is calculated by dividing the distance travelled by the travel time. In advanced work, speed is defined more carefully as the rate of change of distance with time. In any case, speed is a quantity having magnitude only, so it is classified as a scalar.

When the direction of motion as well as its magnitude is important, the correct term to use is **velocity**. Velocity is a vector quantity. Speed is the magnitude of a velocity.

Velocity vectors can be added. When you walk forward in the aisle of an aircraft in flight, the 2-km/hr velocity of your walk adds to the 500-km/hr velocity of the plane, making your total velocity 502 km/hr. When two velocities are not in the same direction, the resultant velocity determined from the addition of two velocity vectors is nevertheless a meaningful, physical quantity.

EXAMPLE 1

A canoeist who can paddle at a speed of 5 km/h in still water wishes to cross a river 400 m wide that has a current of 2 km/h. If he steers the canoe in a direction perpendicular to the current, determine the resultant velocity. Find the point on the opposite bank where the canoe touches.

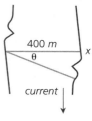

Solution

As the canoe moves through the water, it is carried sideways by the current. So even though its heading is straight across the current, its actual direction of motion is along a line angling downstream determined by the sum of the velocity vectors.

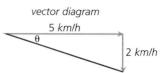

vector diagram

From the vector diagram,

$$|\vec{v}|^2 = (5)^2 + (2)^2 \qquad \text{and} \qquad \tan\theta = \frac{2}{5}$$
$$|\vec{v}| = \sqrt{29} \cong 5.4 \text{ km/h} \qquad\qquad \theta \cong 21.8°$$

Therefore, the canoeist crosses the river at a speed of 5.4 km/h along a line at an angle of about 22°. The displacement triangle is similar to the vector triangle.

$$\frac{x}{2} = \frac{400}{5}$$
$$x = 160$$

He touches the opposite bank at a point 160 m downstream from the point directly opposite his starting point. We could also find x using the angle θ, but we must be careful *not* to round off in the process.

EXAMPLE 2

Suppose the canoeist of Example 1 had wished to travel straight across the river. Determine the direction he must head and the time it will take him to cross the river.

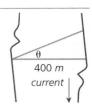

400 m
current

Solution
In order to travel directly across the river, the canoeist must steer the canoe slightly upstream. This time, it is the vector sum, not the heading of the canoe, which is perpendicular to the river bank. From the vector diagram,

vector diagram

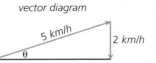

5 km/h   2 km/h

$$|\vec{v}|^2 = (5)^2 - (2)^2 \qquad \text{and} \qquad \sin(\theta) = \frac{2}{5}$$
$$|\vec{v}| = \sqrt{21} \cong 4.6 \text{ km/h} \qquad\qquad \theta \cong 23.6°$$

Therefore, to travel straight across the river, the canoeist must head upstream at an angle of about 24°. His crossing speed will be about 4.6 km/h.

The time it takes to cross the river is calculated from

$$t = \frac{\text{river width}}{\text{crossing speed}} \qquad \text{(where the width is 0.4 km)}$$
$$= \frac{0.4}{\sqrt{21}} \qquad\qquad \text{(we avoid using rounded values if possible)}$$
$$\cong 0.087 \text{ h or 5.2 min}$$

It takes the canoeist approximately 5.2 minutes to cross the river.

Wind affects a plane's speed and direction much the same way that current affects a boat's. The airspeed of a plane is the plane's speed relative to the mass of air it is flying in. This may be different in both magnitude and direction from the plane's ground speed, depending on the strength and direction of the wind.

EXAMPLE 3

An airplane heading northwest at 500 km/h encounters a wind of 120 km/h from 25° north of east. Determine the resultant ground velocity of the plane.

Solution
Since the wind is blowing from 25° north of east, it can be represented by a vector whose direction is west 25° south. This wind will blow the plane off its course,

changing both its ground speed and its heading. Let $|\vec{v}|$ be the airspeed of the plane and $|\vec{w}|$ be the wind speed. On a set of directional axes, draw the two velocity vectors. Then draw the resultant velocity using the parallelogram law of vector addition.

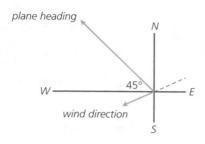 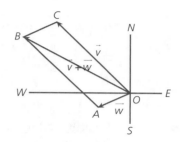

In parallelogram $OCBA$, $\angle COA = 45° + 25° = 70°$, so $\angle OAB = 110°$. Then, in $\triangle OAB$, two sides and the included angle are known, so the magnitude of the resultant velocity can be calculated using the cosine law.

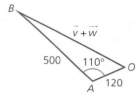

$$|\vec{v} + \vec{w}|^2 = 500^2 + 120^2 - 2(500)(120) \cos 110°$$
$$|\vec{v} + \vec{w}| \cong 552.7$$

Store this answer in your calculator memory.
Next, $\angle AOB$ can be calculated from the sine law.

$$\frac{\sin \angle AOB}{500} = \frac{\sin 110°}{|\vec{v} + \vec{w}|} \qquad \text{(use the value of } |\vec{v} + \vec{w}| \text{ calculated above)}$$

$$\angle AOB \cong 58.2°$$

$$\angle WOB = 58.2° - 25° = 33.2°$$

The resultant velocity has direction 33° north of west and a magnitude of 553 km/h.

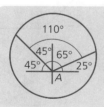

A key step in solving problems such as that in Example 3 is to find an angle in the triangle formed by the vectors. Here is a helpful hint: identify which angle is formed by vectors whose directions are given, and draw small axes at the vertex of that angle. The diagram shows this alternate way to calculate that $\angle OAB = 110°$ in Example 3.

Vectors are needed to describe situations where two objects are moving relative to one another. When astronauts want to dock the space shuttle with the International Space Station, they must match the velocities of the two craft. As they approach, astronauts on each spacecraft can picture themselves to be stationary and the other craft to be moving. When they finally dock, even though the two spacecraft are orbiting the earth at thousands of miles per hour, their **relative velocity** is zero.

Relative velocity is the difference of two velocities. It is what an observer measures, when he perceives himself to be stationary. The principle that *all* velocities are relative was originally formulated by Einstein and became a cornerstone of his Theory of Relativity.

> **When two objects A and B have velocities $\vec{v}_A$ and $\vec{v}_B$, respectively, the velocity of B relative to A is**
> $$\vec{v}_{rel} = \vec{v}_B - \vec{v}_A.$$

EXAMPLE 4

A car travelling east at 110 km/h passes a truck going in the opposite direction at 96 km/h.

a. What is the velocity of the truck relative to the car?

b. The truck turns onto a side road and heads northwest at the same speed. Now what is the velocity of the truck relative to the car?

Solution

The vector diagram shows the velocity vectors of the car and the truck. These velocities are relative to someone standing by the side of the road, watching the two vehicles pass by. Since the car is going east, let its velocity be $\vec{v}_{car} = 110$. Then the truck's velocity is $\vec{v}_{truck} = -96$.

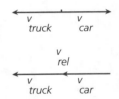

$$\vec{v}_{rel} = \vec{v}_{truck} - \vec{v}_{car}$$
$$= (-96) - (110)$$
$$= -206 \text{ km/h or } 206 \text{ km/h west}$$

This is the velocity that the truck appears to have, according to the driver of the car.

b. After the truck turns, the angle between the car and the truck velocities is 135°. The magnitude of the sum is found using the cosine law.

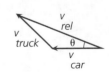

$$|\vec{v}_{rel}|^2 = (96)^2 + (110)^2 - 2(96)(110) \cos 135°$$
$$|\vec{v}_{rel}| \cong 190.4 \text{ km/h}$$

(Store this in your calculator.)

The angle of the relative velocity vector can be calculated from the sine law.

$$\frac{\sin \theta}{96} = \frac{\sin 135°}{190.4}$$
$$\theta \cong 20.9°$$

After the truck turns, its velocity is 190 km/h in a direction $W\ 21°\ N$ relative to the car. Note that the relative velocity of the two vehicles does not depend on their position. It remains the same as long as the two vehicles continue to travel in the same directions without any changes in their velocities.

Exercise 1.4

Part A

1. A plane is heading due east. Will its ground speed be greater than or less than its airspeed, and will its flight path be north or south of east when the wind is from

   a. N b. $S\ 80°\ W$ c. $S\ 30°\ E$ d. $N\ 80°\ E$

2. A man can swim 2 km/h in still water. Find at what angle to the bank he must head if he wishes to swim directly across a river flowing at a speed of

   a. 1 km/h   b. 4 km/h

3. A streetcar, a bus, and a taxi are travelling along a city street at speeds of 35, 42, and 50 km/h, respectively. The streetcar and the taxi are travelling north; the bus is travelling south. Find

   a. the velocity of the streetcar relative to the taxi

   b. the velocity of the streetcar relative to the bus

   c. the velocity of the taxi relative to the bus

   d. the velocity of the bus relative to the streetcar

Part B

4. A river is 2 km wide and flows at 6 km/h. A motor boat that has a speed of 20 km/h in still water heads out from one bank perpendicular to the current. A marina lies directly across the river on the opposite bank.

   a. How far downstream from the marina will the boat reach the other bank?

   b. How long will it take?

5. An airplane is headed north with a constant velocity of 450 km/h. The plane encounters a west wind blowing at 100 km/h.

   a. How far will the plane travel in 3 h?

   b. What is the direction of the plane?

6. A light plane is travelling at 175 km/h on a heading of $N\ 8°\ E$ in a 40-km/h wind from $N\ 80°\ E$. Determine the plane's ground velocity.

7. A boat heads 15° west of north with a water speed of 3 m/s. Determine its velocity relative to the ground when there is a 2 m/s current from 40° east of north.

8. A plane is steering east at a speed of 240 km/h. What is the ground speed of the plane if the wind is from the northwest at 65 km/h? What is the plane's actual direction?

9. Upon reaching a speed of 215 km/h on the runway, a jet raises its nose to an angle of 18° with the horizontal and begins to lift off the ground.

   a. Calculate the horizontal and vertical components of its velocity at this moment.

   b. What is the physical interpretation of each of these components of the jet's velocity?

10. A pilot wishes to fly to an airfield $S\ 20°\ E$ of his present position. If the average airspeed of the plane is 520 km/h and the wind is from $N\ 80°\ E$ at 46 km/h,

    a. in what direction should the pilot steer?

    b. what will the plane's ground speed be?

11. A destroyer detects a submarine 8 nautical miles due east travelling northeast at 20 knots. If the destroyer has a top speed of 30 knots, at what heading should it travel to intercept the submarine?

Part C

12. An airplane flies from Toronto to Vancouver and back. Determine which time is shorter.

    a. The time for the round trip when there is a constant wind blowing from Vancouver to Toronto

    b. The time for the round trip when there is no wind

13. A sailor climbs a mast at 0.5 m/s on a ship travelling north at 12 m/s, while the current flows east at 3 m/s. What is the speed of the sailor relative to the ocean floor?

14. A car is 260 m north and a truck is 170 m west of an intersection. They are both approaching the intersection, the car from the north at 80 km/h, and the truck from the west at 50 km/h. Determine the velocity of the truck relative to the car.

Key Concepts Review

In this chapter, you have been introduced to the concept of a vector and have seen some applications of vectors. Perhaps the most important mathematical skill to develop from this chapter is that of combining vectors through vector addition, both graphically and algebraically.

Diagrams drawn free hand are sufficient, but try to make them realistic. It is not difficult to draw angles that are correct to within about 10° and to make lengths roughly proportional to the magnitudes of the vectors in a problem.

Once you have calculated answers, ask yourself if the calculated angles and magnitudes are consistent with your diagram, and if they are physically reasonable.

SUMS

Speaking informally, if you want to go from A to C you can travel directly along the vector $\overrightarrow{AC}$, or you can detour through B, travelling first along $\overrightarrow{AB}$, and then along $\overrightarrow{BC}$. This means that $\overrightarrow{AC} = \overrightarrow{AB} + \overrightarrow{BC}$, but observe how the detour point fits into the equation: it is the second letter of the first vector and the first letter of the second vector.

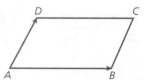

DIFFERENCES

Using the same diagram, if you want to go from D to B, you can travel directly along $\overrightarrow{DB}$, or you can detour through A, travelling first backwards along $\overrightarrow{AD}$, and then forwards along $\overrightarrow{AB}$. This translates into the equation $\overrightarrow{DB} = -\overrightarrow{AD} + \overrightarrow{AB}$, which of course is just the difference $\overrightarrow{DB} = \overrightarrow{AB} - \overrightarrow{AD}$. Note carefully that, on the right hand side of the equation, the order of the initial point D and the end point B are reversed, and the detour point is the initial letter of the two vectors.

Pay attention to and become familiar with details such as these. You will be able to draw and interpret vector diagrams and handle vector equations more quickly and correctly if you do.

Brain cells in the superior colliculus are tuned to the directions of distant visual and auditory stimuli. Each cell responds only to stimuli located within a cone of directions. The vigour of a cell's response can be regarded as specifying the magnitude of a vector in the direction the cell represents. The resultant vector formed by summing the vectors represented by the individual cells points in the direction of the stimulus.

Dr. Randy Gallistel, a professor in the Department of Psychology at UCLA, whose research focus is in the cognitive neurosciences, has suggested that these neurological resultant vectors are "the first new idea about how the nervous system represents the value of a variable since the beginning of the [twentieth] century (from *Conservations in the Cognitive Neurosciences*, Ed. Michael S. Gazzaniga, MA: Bradford Books/MIT Press, 1997)."

Investigate and Apply

1. What direction would be represented by a north cell responding three times as vigorously as a northeast cell, which, in turn, is responding twice as vigorously as an east cell?

2. Consider an ensemble of 36 cells, representing directions evenly distributed around a circle, with one cell representing north. One cell will represent 10° east of north, the next will represent 20° east of north, and so on. A cell always responds to some extent whenever a stimulus is within 20° of the cell's direction.

   a) Which cells will respond to a stimulus whose direction is northeast?
   b) A *response pattern* is a description of the relative proportions of the vigour of the various cells' responses. Give two possible response patterns for the cells found in part **a**.

3. How do you think the brain deals with the fact that several different response patterns can represent the same direction?

INDEPENDENT STUDY

Investigate the field of neuroscience.

What other things can be represented in the brain using resultant vectors formed from cells representing individual vectors?

What are some other questions to which neuroscientists are seeking answers?

What role does mathematics play in the search for answers to these questions? ●

Review Exercise

1. a. If $\vec{v} + \vec{t} = \vec{v}$, what is $\vec{t}$?

   b. If $t\vec{v} = \vec{v}$, what is t?

   c. If $s\vec{v} = t\vec{u}$, and $\vec{u}$ is not parallel to $\vec{v}$, what are s and t?

2. Using vector diagrams, show that

   a. $(a + b)\vec{u} = a\vec{u} + b\vec{u}$ b. $(ab)\vec{u} = a(b\vec{u})$

3. A mass M is hung on a line between two supports A and B.

   a. Which part of the line supporting the mass has the greater tension? Explain.

   b. The supports A and B are not at the same level. What effect does this have on the tension in the line? Explain.

4. Explain these properties of the zero vector:

   a. $0\vec{v} = \vec{0}$ b. $\vec{v} + \vec{0} = \vec{v}$ c. if $\vec{u} + \vec{v} = \vec{0}$, then $\vec{u} = -\vec{v}$

5. If $\hat{i}$ and $\hat{j}$ are perpendicular unit vectors, what is the magnitude of

   a. $3\hat{i} + 4\hat{j}$?   b. $24\hat{i} - 7\hat{j}$?   c. $a\hat{i} + b\hat{j}$?

6. Show that $|\vec{a}| + |\vec{b}| = |\vec{a} - \vec{b}|$, if $\vec{a}$ and $\vec{b}$ have opposite directions.

7. A 3-kg mass is hanging from the end of a string. If a horizontal force of 12 N pulls the mass to the side

   a. find the tension in the string

   b. find the angle the string makes with the vertical

8. Two forces $\vec{F}_1$ and $\vec{F}_2$ act on an object. Determine the magnitude of the resultant if

   a. $|\vec{F}_1| = 54\ N$, $|\vec{F}_2| = 34\ N$, and the angle between them is $55°$

   b. $|\vec{F}_1| = 21\ N$, $|\vec{F}_2| = 45\ N$, and the angle between them is $140°$

9. Two forces at an angle of $130°$ to each other act on an object. Determine their magnitudes if the resultant has a magnitude of 480 N and makes an angle of $55°$ with one of the forces.

10. Forces of 5 N, 2 N, and 12 N, all lying in the same plane, act on an object. The 5 N and 2 N forces lie on opposite sides of the 12 N force at angles of 40° and 20°, respectively. Find the magnitude and direction of the resultant.

11. A 10-kg mass is supported by two strings of length 5 m and 7 m attached to two points in the ceiling 10 m apart. Find the tension in each string.

12. The pilot of an airplane that flies at 800 km/h wishes to travel to a city 800 km due east. There is a 80 km/h wind from the northeast.

    a. What should the plane's heading be?

    b. How long will the trip take?

13. An airplane heads due south with an air speed of 480 km/h. Measurements made from the ground indicate that the plane's ground speed is 528 km/h at 15° east of south. Calculate the wind speed.

14. A camp counsellor leaves a dock paddling a canoe at 3 m/s. She heads downstream at 30° to the current, which is flowing at 4 m/s.

    a. How far downstream does she travel in 10 s?

    b. What is the length of time required to cross the river if its width is 150 m?

15. A pilot wishes to reach an airport 350 km from his present position at a heading of N 60° E. If the wind is from S 25° E with a speed of 73 km/h, and the plane has an airspeed of 450 km/h, find

    a. what heading the pilot should steer

    b. what the ground speed of the plane will be

    c. how many minutes it will take for the plane to reach its destination

16. A coast guard cutter is steering west at 12 knots, when its radar detects a tanker ahead at a distance of 9 nautical miles travelling with a relative velocity of 19 knots, on a heading of E 14° N. What is the actual velocity of the tanker?

17. Twice a week, a cruise ship carries vacationers from Miami, Florida to Freeport in the Bahamas, and then on to Nassau before returning to Miami. The distance from Miami to Freeport is 173 km on a heading of E 20° N. The distance from Freeport to Nassau is 217 km on a heading of E 50° S. Once a week the ship travels directly from Miami to Nassau. Determine the displacement vector from Miami to Nassau.

18. If $a\vec{u} + b\vec{v} = \vec{0}$ and $\vec{u}$ and $\vec{v}$ have different directions, what must a and b equal?

19. Show geometrically that $\left| \,|\vec{u}| - |\vec{v}|\, \right| \leq |\vec{u} + \vec{v}|$. Under what conditions does equality hold?

Chapter 1 Test

1. Under what conditions is $|\vec{u} + \vec{v}| = |\vec{u}| + |\vec{v}|$?

2. Copy the three given vectors $\vec{a}$, $\vec{b}$, and $\vec{c}$ onto graph paper, then accurately draw the following three vectors.

   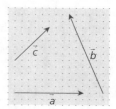

   a. $\vec{u} = \vec{a} + 3\vec{c}$
   b. $\vec{v} = \vec{b} - \vec{a}$
   c. $\vec{w} = \frac{2}{3}\vec{b} - 5\vec{c} + \vec{a}$

3. Simplify $3(4\vec{u} + \vec{v}) - 2\vec{u} - 3(\vec{u} - \vec{v})$.

4. Illustrate in a diagram the vector property $4(\vec{a} + \vec{b}) = 4\vec{a} + 4\vec{b}$. What is this property called?

5. Forces of 15 N and 11 N act on a point at 125° to each other. Find the magnitude of the resultant.

6. A steel cable 14 m long is suspended between two fixed points 10 m apart horizontally. The cable supports a mass of 50 kg at a point 6 m from one end. Determine the tension in each part of the cable.

7. A ferry boat crosses a river and arrives at a point on the opposite bank directly across from its starting point. The boat can travel at 4 m/s and the current is 1.5 m/s. If the river is 650 m wide at the crossing point, in what direction must the boat steer and how long will it take to cross?

8. What is the relative velocity of an airplane travelling at a speed of 735 knots on a heading of $E\ 70°\ S$ with respect to an aircraft at the same height steering $W\ 50°\ S$ at a speed of 300 knots?

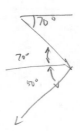

The word *geometry* comes from the Greek words for *earth* and *measure*. When we solve geometrical problems, the rules or assumptions we make are chosen to match our experience with the world we live in. For example, since locally the earth looks flat, it makes sense to talk about planar figures such as triangles, circles, and so on. But what happens if we change the rules? For example, we normally define distance in Euclidean terms. When we represent points and figures in terms of coordinates on the Cartesian plane, then the distance between two points $P(x_1, y_1)$ and $Q(x_2, y_2)$ is

$$d(P, Q) = \sqrt{(x_1 - x_2)^2 + (y_1 - y_2)^2}$$

If we ask for the locus of all points that are a constant distance, say 1, from the given point $(0, 0)$, we get the circle with equation $x^2 + y^2 = 1$.

One way to create a whole new geometry is to change the way we measure distance. For example, we can use the so-called taxi-cab distance given by

$$t(P, Q) = |x_1 - x_2| + |y_1 - y_2|$$

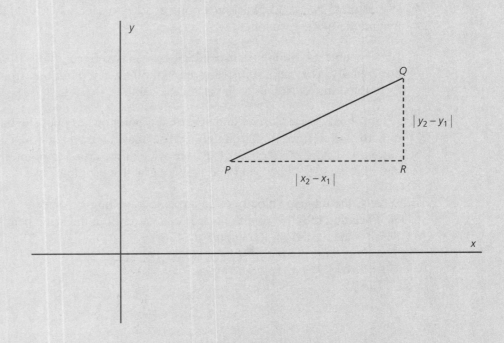

The taxi-cab distance between P and Q is the sum of the lengths PR and RQ. The reason for the colourful name is that it is the actual distance driven if a cab is restricted to a rectangular grid of streets. Note that $t(P, Q) \le d(p, Q)$ for any pair of points P and Q.

With this definition of distance, we can ask the same locus question. What is the set of all points a taxi-cab distance of 1 from the origin? If $P(x, y)$ is any point on the locus, then the equation of the locus is $|x - 0| + |y - 0| = 1$ or $|x| + |y| = 1$. The locus is plotted below, and turns out to be a square. The graph can be produced by a graphing calculator or by hand. In this case, it is easiest to break the problem into four cases depending on x and y being positive or negative.

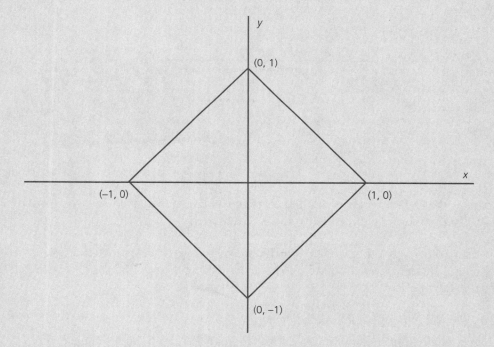

You can investigate many other locus problems in this new geometry. For example, find the set of points that are equidistant from $(0, 0)$ and $(1, 1)$. If we use Euclidean distance, we get a straight line, the right bisector of the line segment joining the two points. The following diagram shows what happens with taxi-cab distance.

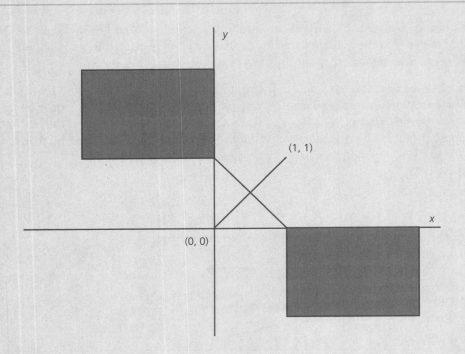

For $0 \leq x \leq 1$, the right bisector is the line, as with Euclidean distance. However, for $x \geq 1$, $y \leq 0$ and $x \leq 0$, $y \geq 1$, all points are equidistant from $(0, 0)$ and $(1, 1)$.

There are many other ways to generate non-Euclidean geometries. Another example is to look at geometry on the surface of a sphere. In this geometry, straight lines (the shortest path between two points) become arcs of circles.

For fun, try the following with taxi-cab distance:

1. Find an equilateral triangle with taxi-cab side length 1. Are all angles equal?

2. Sketch the locus of all points that are equidistant from $(0, 0)$ and $(1, 2)$.

3. The line segment joining $(0, 0)$ to $(1, 0)$ is rotated about the origin. What happens to its length?

Chapter 2

ALGEBRAIC VECTORS AND APPLICATIONS

For quantities that have both magnitude and direction, the directed line segment or arrow is an excellent introductory method. But what about a quantity that has more than three dimensions? In such cases, an algebraic vector model is required. A vector model allows you to add, subtract, and multiply by a scalar vector. We can also use this model to multiply one vector by another vector. The development of the vector model was made possible because, thanks to Descartes and analytic geometry, many geometric ideas already had an algebraic counterpart. For example, a line could be represented by a picture or by an equation. We will see the real power of vectors in this chapter, when we will use them to solve problems in the third dimension and beyond.

CHAPTER EXPECTATIONS In this chapter, you will

- determine equations of lines in two- and three-dimensional space, **Section 2.1**
- determine the intersection of a line and a plane in three-dimensional space, **Section 2.1**
- represent Cartesian vectors, **Section 2.1, 2.2**
- determine and interpret dot and cross products of geometric vectors, **Section 2.3, 2.4, 2.5**
- perform mathematical operations on Cartesian vectors, **Section 2.3, 2.4, 2.5**

Atoms bond together to form the molecules that make up the substances around us. The geometry of molecules is a factor in determining many of the chemical properties of these substances. Ethyl alcohol and dimethyl ether are both formed from two carbon atoms, six hydrogen atoms, and one oxygen atom (C_2H_6O), but they have very different chemical and physical attributes. The properties of enzymes, protein molecules that speed up biochemical reactions, depend upon precise fits between molecules with specific shapes. One aspect of molecular geometry that interests chemists is called the bond angle. It is the angle between two bonds in a molecule. For example, the angle formed where two hydrogen atoms link to an oxygen atom to form water (H_2O) is about 104.5°.

Investigate

A water molecule can be studied in a Cartesian plane. If we allow each unit on the plane to represent 10^{-11} metres and place the oxygen atom at the origin, then the hydrogen atoms are located symmetrically at about (7.59, 5.88) and (−7.59, 5.88). The bond angle formed at the oxygen atom is

$$\theta = 180 - 2 \times \tan^{-1}\left(\frac{5.88}{7.59}\right) = 104.5°.$$

Can you explain why this calculation is correct?

Nitrogen trioxide (NO_3^-) is an example of a trigonal planar molecule. It consists of four atoms in a plane: three oxygen atoms surrounding and individually bonding to a single nitrogen atom. Because there are three identical atoms surrounding the nitrogen atom, the three are evenly spaced around a circle. The bond angle for each of the three bonds is, therefore, 360 ÷ 3 = 120°.

DISCUSSION QUESTIONS

1. If the distance between the nitrogen atom and each oxygen atom in NO_3^- is 1.22×10^{-10} metres, what is one way to assign planar coordinates to the atoms?

2. Formaldehyde (H_2CO) is a trigonal planar molecule with the carbon in the centre. The bond between the carbon and the oxygen is shorter than the bond between the carbon and either one of the hydrogen atoms. Which is likely to be smaller, the O-C-H bond angle or the H-C-H bond angle?

$$
\begin{array}{c}
\text{O} \\
\| \\
\text{C} \\
/ \quad \backslash \\
\text{H} \quad \text{H}
\end{array}
$$

Formaldehyde

3. Can three-atom molecules always be studied in a plane? Can four-atom molecules always be studied in a plane? What about molecules with more than four atoms? ●

Section 2.1 — Algebraic Vectors

In this chapter, we establish principles that allow the use of algebraic methods in the study of vectors. The application of algebra to problems in geometry first became possible in 1637, when Descartes introduced the concept of a **coordinate system.**

A line is a geometrical object. How is a coordinate system for a line constructed? First, choose an arbitrary point on the line as a reference point, or origin. Next, associate with each point P on the line a real number a. How? Let the sign of a indicate which side of the origin P is on, and let the magnitude of a represent the distance from the origin to P. The result is known as the real number line, and a is called the coordinate of P.

The correspondence between points on the line and real numbers is complete in this sense: each point on the line has a different real number as its coordinate, and every real number corresponds to one and only one point on the line.

Now let $\vec{u}$ be a vector on this line. Move the vector until its initial point is at the origin. Its endpoint will fall on some point P with coordinate a. The coordinate a contains everything you need to describe the vector $\vec{u}$.

The absolute value $|a|$ is the magnitude of $\vec{u}$, and the sign of a tells you its direction.

We have now established the connection between the coordinates of a point and a geometrical vector on a line. This amounts to an algebraic representation of a geometrical vector. It is the first step in the development of algebraic methods to handle vector problems.

A line is one-dimensional. A plane has two dimensions. But the same process leads to an algebraic representation of a vector in a plane. The Cartesian coordinate system for a plane is constructed from two real number lines— the x-axis and the y-axis—placed at right angles in the plane. The axes are oriented so that a counter-clockwise rotation about the origin carries the positive x-axis into the positive y-axis. Any point P in the plane is identified by an ordered pair of real numbers (a, b), which are its coordinates.

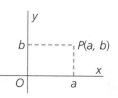

Let $\vec{u}$ be a vector in the plane. Move $\vec{u}$ until its initial point is at the origin. Its endpoint will fall on some point P with coordinates (a, b). The magnitude of $\vec{u}$ can be determined from (a, b) using the Pythagorean Theorem. The direction of $\vec{u}$ can be expressed in terms of the angle θ between $\vec{u}$ and the positive x-axis.

We can observe that, just as in the case of a line, the magnitude and direction of $\vec{u}$ are determined entirely by the coordinates of P. Nothing else is needed. Therefore, the ordered pair (a, b) is a valid representation of the vector $\vec{u}$.

> Any vector $\vec{u}$ in a plane can be written as an ordered pair (a, b), where its magnitude $|\vec{u}|$ and direction θ are given by the equations
>
> $$|\vec{u}| = \sqrt{a^2 + b^2} \quad \text{and} \quad \theta = \tan^{-1}\left(\frac{b}{a}\right)$$
>
> with θ measured counter-clockwise from the positive x-axis to the line of the vector. The formula above gives two values of θ, $0 \le \theta < 360°$. The actual value depends on the quadrant in which P(a, b) lies.

The ordered pair (a, b) is referred to as an algebraic vector. The values of a and b are the x- and y-components of the vector.

It is important to remember that the ordered pair (a, b) can be interpreted in two different ways: it can represent either a point with coordinates a and b, or a vector with components a and b. The context of a problem will tell you whether (a, b) represents a point or a vector.

EXAMPLE 1

The position vector of a point P is the vector $\overrightarrow{OP}$ from the origin to the point. Draw the position vector of the point P(−3, 7), express it in ordered pair notation, and determine its magnitude and direction.

Solution

The point P(−3, 7) is in the second quadrant. The position vector of P is $\overrightarrow{OP} = (-3, 7)$. The magnitude and direction of $\overrightarrow{OP}$ are calculated as follows:

$$|\overrightarrow{OP}|^2 = (-3)^2 + (7)^2 \qquad \tan\theta = \frac{7}{-3}$$
$$|\overrightarrow{OP}| = \sqrt{58} \qquad\qquad \theta \cong 113°$$

Thus, the magnitude of $\overrightarrow{OP}$ is $\sqrt{58}$. Its direction makes an angle of approximately 113° with the positive x-axis.

Another notation commonly used to describe algebraic vectors in a plane employs unit vectors. Define the vectors $\hat{i} = (1, 0)$ and $\hat{j} = (0, 1)$. These are unit vectors that point in the direction of the positive x-axis and positive y-axis, respectively.

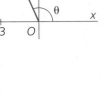

As you can see in the diagram, the position vector of point $P(a, b)$, and thus any vector $\vec{u}$ in the plane, can be expressed as the vector sum of scalar multiples of $\hat{i}$ and $\hat{j}$.

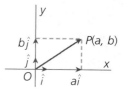

Ordered pair notation and unit vector notation are equivalent. Any algebraic vector can be written in either form:

$$\vec{u} = \overrightarrow{OP} = (a, b) \quad \text{or} \quad \vec{u} = \overrightarrow{OP} = a\hat{i} + b\hat{j}$$

EXAMPLE 2

Express the position vector of each of the points shown in the diagram as an ordered pair and in unit vector notation.

Solution

$\overrightarrow{OP} = (6, -2)$ $\overrightarrow{OQ} = (-3, 3)$ $\overrightarrow{OR} = (0, 7)$
$\phantom{\overrightarrow{OP}} = 6\hat{i} - 2\hat{j}$ $\phantom{\overrightarrow{OQ}} = -3\hat{i} + 3\hat{j}$ $\phantom{\overrightarrow{OR}} = 7\hat{j}$

A coordinate system for three-dimensional space is formed in much the same way as a coordinate system for a two-dimensional plane. Some point in space is chosen as the origin. Through the origin, three mutually perpendicular number lines are drawn, called the x-axis, the y-axis, and the z-axis. Each point in space corresponds to an ordered triple of real numbers (a, b, c), which are its coordinates on the three axes.

There are two different ways to choose the positive directions of the axes. As a rule, mathematicians use a right-handed coordinate system. If you could grasp the z-axis of a right-handed system with your right hand, pointing your thumb in the direction of the positive z-axis, your fingers should curl from the positive x-axis toward the positive y-axis. A left-handed system would have the positive y-axis oriented in the opposite direction.

A plane in space that contains two of the coordinate axes is known as a coordinate plane. The plane containing the x- and y-axes, for instance, is called the xy-plane. The other two coordinate planes are named similarly. A point such as $(-4, 0, 1)$, which has a y-coordinate of 0, lies in the xz-plane.

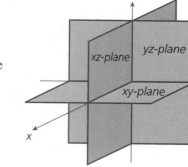

To plot a point $P(a, b, c)$ in space, move a units from the origin in the x direction, then b units in the y direction, and then c units in the z direction. Be sure each move is made along a line parallel to the corresponding axis. Drawing a rectangular box will help you to see the three-dimensional aspect of such diagrams.

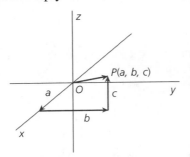 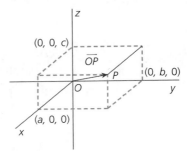

Just as in two dimensions, any vector in space can be placed with its initial point at the origin. Its tip will then fall on some point P with coordinates (a, b, c), from which its magnitude and direction can be determined. The ordered triple (a, b, c), therefore, represents an algebraic vector in three dimensions. Alternatively, this vector could be expressed in terms of unit vectors $\hat{i}, \hat{j}$, and $\hat{k}$, where $\hat{i} = (1, 0, 0)$, $\hat{j} = (0, 1, 0)$, and $\hat{k} = (0, 0, 1)$.

Any vector $\vec{u}$ in three-dimensional space can be written
as an ordered triple, $\vec{u} = \overrightarrow{OP} = (a, b, c)$,
or in terms of unit vectors, $\vec{u} = \overrightarrow{OP} = a\hat{i} + b\hat{j} + c\hat{k}$.
Its magnitude is given by $|\vec{u}| = \sqrt{a^2 + b^2 + c^2}$.

EXAMPLE 3

Locate the point P, sketch the position vector $\overrightarrow{OP}$ in three dimensions, and calculate its magnitude.

a. $P(-5, -7, 2)$

b. $\overrightarrow{OP} = 3\hat{i} + 5\hat{j} - 4\hat{k}$

Solution

a.

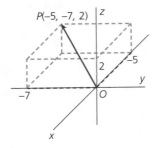

b.

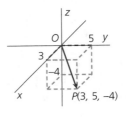

$$|\overrightarrow{OP}| = \sqrt{(-5)^2 + (-7)^2 + (2)^2}$$
$$= \sqrt{78}$$

$$|\overrightarrow{OP}| = \sqrt{(3)^2 + (5)^2 + (-4)^2}$$
$$= \sqrt{50}$$

In two dimensions, we can describe the direction of a vector by a single angle. In three dimensions, we use three angles, called direction angles.

The **direction angles** of a vector (a, b, c) are the angles α, β, and γ that the vector makes with the positive x-, y-, and z-axes, respectively, where $0° \leq \alpha, \beta, \gamma \leq 180°$.

In this context, the components a, b, and c of the vector $\vec{u}$ are referred to as direction numbers.

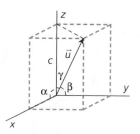

In the given diagram, the direction angles are all acute angles. We can see the right triangle that relates $\vec{u}$, the direction number c, and the direction angle γ,

from which it follows that $\cos \gamma = \frac{c}{|\vec{u}|}$.

The other direction numbers and angles are related in the same way.

The **direction cosines** of a vector are the cosines of the direction angles α, β and γ, where

$$\cos \alpha = \frac{a}{|\vec{u}|}, \cos \beta = \frac{b}{|\vec{u}|}, \text{ and } \cos \gamma = \frac{c}{|\vec{u}|}.$$

Note that if you divide a vector (a, b, c) by its magnitude $\vec{u}$, you create a unit vector with components $\left(\frac{a}{|\vec{u}|}, \frac{b}{|\vec{u}|}, \frac{c}{|\vec{u}|}\right)$, which is exactly $(\cos \alpha, \cos \beta, \cos \gamma)$. Thus, the direction cosines are the components of a unit vector. Consequently,

$$\cos^2 \alpha + \cos^2 \beta + \cos^2 \gamma = 1.$$

It follows from this that the direction cosines, and hence the direction angles, are not all independent. From any two of them you can find the third.

EXAMPLE 4

Find the direction cosines and the direction angles of the vector $\vec{u} = (0, 5, -3)$.

Solution
The magnitude of $\vec{u}$ is $\sqrt{(0)^2 + (5)^2 + (-3)^2} = \sqrt{34}$.
The direction cosines and angles are therefore

$\cos \alpha = \dfrac{0}{\sqrt{34}}, \qquad \alpha = 90°$

$\cos \beta = \dfrac{5}{\sqrt{34}}, \qquad \beta \cong 31°$

$\cos \gamma = \dfrac{-3}{\sqrt{34}}, \qquad \gamma \cong 121°$

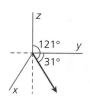

This vector is perpendicular to the x-axis, and is, therefore, parallel to the yz-plane.

EXAMPLE 5

A vector $\vec{u}$ makes angles of 60° and 105°, respectively, with the x- and y-axes. What is the angle between $\vec{u}$ and the z-axis?

Solution

$\cos^2 60° + \cos^2 105° + \cos^2 \gamma = 1$

$\cos \gamma = \pm \sqrt{1 - \cos^2 60° - \cos^2 105°}$

$\gamma \cong 34°$ or $146°$

The angle between $\vec{u}$ and the z-axis is 34° or 146°, so there are two possible vectors.

Exercise 2.1

Part A

1. What is the difference between an algebraic vector and a geometric vector?

2. Rewrite each of the following vectors in the form $a\hat{i} + b\hat{j}$.
   a. $(-5, 2)$ b. $(0, 6)$ c. $(-1, 6)$

3. Rewrite each of the following vectors as an ordered pair.
   a. $2\hat{i} + \hat{j}$ b. $-3\hat{i}$ c. $5\hat{i} - 5\hat{j}$

4. Rewrite each of the following vectors in the form $a\hat{i} + b\hat{j} + c\hat{k}$.
   a. $(-2, 1, 1)$ b. $(3, 4, -3)$ c. $(0, 4, -1)$ d. $(-2, 0, 7)$

5. Rewrite each of the following vectors as an ordered triple.
   a. $3\hat{i} - 8\hat{j} + \hat{k}$ b. $-2\hat{i} - 2\hat{j} - 5\hat{k}$
   c. $2\hat{j} + 6\hat{k}$ d. $-4\hat{i} + 9\hat{j}$

6. Express each of the following vectors as an algebraic vector in the form (a, b).
   a. $|\vec{u}| = 12, \theta = 135°$ b. $|\vec{v}| = 36, \theta = 330°$
   c. $|\vec{w}| = 16, \theta = 190°$ d. $|\vec{x}| = 13, \theta = 270°$

7. Express each of the following vectors as a geometric vector by stating its magnitude and direction.

   a. $\vec{u} = (-6\sqrt{3}, 6)$

   c. $\vec{w} = (4, 3)$

   b. $\vec{v} = (-4\sqrt{3}, -12)$

   d. $\vec{x} = (0, 8)$

8. What vector is represented in each of the following diagrams?

   a.

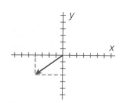

   b.

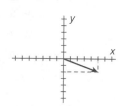

   c.

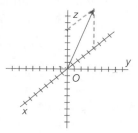

   d.

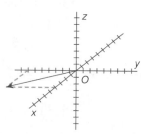

   e.

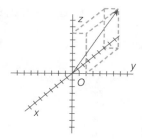

   f.

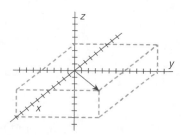

9. For each of the following, draw the x-axis, y-axis, and z-axis, and accurately plot the points.

   $A(-3, 0, 0)$ $B(0, 2, 0)$ $C(0, 0, -2)$ $D(-3, 2, 0)$

   $E(3, 0, -2)$ $F(0, 2, 3)$ $G(-2, 0, 3)$ $H(0, 3, -2)$

Part B

10. Describe where each of the following sets of points is located.

   a. $(0, 0, 6), (0, 0, -3), (0, 0, 4)$ b. $(0, 2, 8), (0, -8, 2), (0, -2, 2)$

   c. $(3, 0, 3), (3, 0, -5), (-3, 0, 5)$ d. $(-1, 2, 0), (0, 4, 0), (5, -6, 0)$

   e. $(1, 3, -2), (1, 3, 6), (1, 3, 11)$ f. $(2, 2, 2), (-3, -3, -3), (8, 8, 8)$

11. Where are the following general points located?

   a. $A(x, y, 0)$
   b. $B(x, 0, 0)$
   c. $C(0, y, z)$
   d. $D(0, 0, z)$
   e. $E(x, 0, z)$
   f. $F(0, y, 0)$

12. For each of the following, draw the x-axis, y-axis, and z-axis and accurately draw the position vectors.

   a. $M(6, -4, 2)$
   b. $N(-3, 5, 3)$
   c. $P(2, 3, -7)$
   d. $Q(-4, -9, 5)$
   e. $R(5, -5, -1)$
   f. $T(-6, 1, -8)$

13. Find the magnitude and the direction of the following vectors.

   a. $\overrightarrow{OE} = (1, 7)$
   b. $\overrightarrow{OF} = (0, -6)$
   c. $\overrightarrow{OG} = (-9, 12)$
   d. $\overrightarrow{OH} = \left(-\frac{1}{2}, \frac{\sqrt{3}}{2}\right)$
   e. $\overrightarrow{OJ} = \left(\frac{2}{\sqrt{5}}, -\frac{\sqrt{6}}{\sqrt{5}}\right)$
   f. $\overrightarrow{OK} = (-\sqrt{6}, 0)$

14. Find the magnitude of the following vectors.

   a. $(-12, -4, 6)$
   b. $(8, -27, 21)$
   c. $\left(\frac{14}{27}, \frac{-22}{27}, \frac{-7}{27}\right)$
   d. $(-\sqrt{2}, 2\sqrt{3}, \sqrt{2})$

15. Can the sum of two unit vectors be a unit vector? Explain. Can the difference?

16. a. Calculate $|\vec{a}|$ when $\vec{a} = (2, 3, -2)$.
    b. Find $\frac{1}{|\vec{a}|}\vec{a}$. Is it a unit vector?

17. a. Find the magnitude of the vector $\vec{v} = 2\hat{i} - 3\hat{j} - 6\hat{k}$.
    b. Find a unit vector in the direction of $\vec{v}$.

18. If $\vec{v} = (3, 4, 12)$, find a unit vector in the direction opposite to $\vec{v}$.

19. Show that any unit vector in two dimensions can be written as $(\cos \theta, \sin \theta)$, where θ is the angle between the vector and the x-axis.

20. Reposition each of the following vectors so that its initial point is at the origin, and determine its components.

   a.
   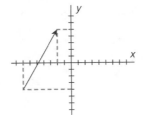

   b.
   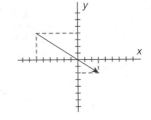

c.

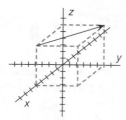

d.

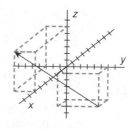

21. Draw a diagram of a vector $\vec{u} = (a, b, c)$ that illustrates the relationship between

    a. $\vec{u}$, a, and $\cos \alpha$ (α acute) b. $\vec{u}$, b, and $\cos \beta$ (β obtuse)

22. The direction angles of a vector are all equal. Find the direction angles to the nearest degree.

Part C

23. Prove that the magnitude of the vector $\overrightarrow{OP} = (a, b, c)$ is given by $|\overrightarrow{OP}| = \sqrt{a^2 + b^2 + c^2}$.

24. Give a geometrical interpretation of the vector $\vec{u} = (4, 2, -5, 2)$. Make a reasonable conjecture about its magnitude.

As we saw in Section 2.1, all vectors can be expressed in terms of the unit vectors $\hat{i}$ and $\hat{j}$ in two dimensions, or $\hat{i}, \hat{j}$, and $\hat{k}$ in three dimensions, or, equivalently, in terms of ordered pairs or triplets. Vectors such as $\hat{i}, \hat{j}$, and $\hat{k}$, which have been chosen to play this special role, are termed **basis vectors.** They form a basis for the two- or three-dimensional spaces in which vectors exist. In Example 1, we establish the uniqueness of the algebraic representation of a vector in terms of these basis vectors.

EXAMPLE 1

Prove that the representation of a two-dimensional algebraic vector in terms of its x- and y-components is unique.

Solution

Using the method of proof by contradiction, we begin by assuming that the vector $\vec{u}$ can be written in terms of components in two different ways:

$$\vec{u} = a_1\hat{i} + b_1\hat{j} \quad \text{and} \quad \vec{u} = a_2\hat{i} + b_2\hat{j}$$

Since they represent the same vector, these expressions must be equal.

$$a_1\hat{i} + b_1\hat{j} = a_2\hat{i} + b_2 j$$

Some rearrangement produces the equations

$$a_1\hat{i} - a_2\hat{i} = -b_1\hat{j} + b_2\hat{j}$$
$$(a_1 - a_2)\hat{i} = (-b_1 + b_2)\hat{j}$$

The last equation states that a scalar multiple of $\hat{i}$ equals a scalar multiple of $\hat{j}$. But this cannot be true. The unit vectors $\hat{i}$ and $\hat{j}$ have different directions, and no multiplication by a scalar can make the vectors equal. The only possible way the equation can be valid is if the coefficients of $\hat{i}$ and $\hat{j}$ are zero, that is, $a_1 = a_2$ and $b_1 = b_2$, which means that the two representations of the vector $\vec{u}$ are not different after all.

The uniqueness of algebraic vectors leads to a fundamental statement about the equality of algebraic vectors.

> **Two algebraic vectors** are equal if and only if their respective Cartesian components are equal.

Since all vectors can be expressed in terms of the basis vectors $\hat{i}, \hat{j}$, and $\hat{k}$, all the rules of vector algebra discussed in Chapter 1 apply to algebraic vectors. In two dimensions, for instance, scalar multiplication of a vector and addition of two vectors, written in both unit vector and ordered pair notation, look like this:

scalar multiplication
$$k(a\hat{i} + b\hat{j}) = ka\hat{i} + kb\hat{j}$$
or
$$k(a, b) = (ka, kb)$$

vector addition
$$(a_1\hat{i} + b_1\hat{j}) + (a_2\hat{i} + b_2\hat{j}) = (a_1 + a_2)\hat{i} + (b_1 + b_2)\hat{j}$$
or
$$(a_1, b_1) + (a_2, b_2) = (a_1 + a_2, b_1 + b_2)$$

EXAMPLE 2

If $\vec{u} = (5, -7)$ and $\vec{v} = (-2, 3)$, find $\vec{w} = 6\vec{u} - 4\vec{v}$.

Solution

In ordered pair notation
$\vec{w} = 6\vec{u} - 4\vec{v}$
$\quad = 6(5, -7) - 4(-2, 3)$
$\quad = (30, -42) + (8, -12)$
$\quad = (38, -54)$

In unit vector notation
$\vec{w} = 6\vec{u} - 4\vec{v}$
$\quad = 6(5\hat{i} - 7\hat{j}) - 4(-2\hat{i} + 3\hat{j})$
$\quad = 30\hat{i} - 42\hat{j} + 8\hat{i} - 12\hat{j}$
$\quad = 38\hat{i} - 54\hat{j}$

EXAMPLE 3

Using vectors, demonstrate that the three points $A(5, -1)$, $B(-3, 4)$, and $C(13, -6)$ are collinear.

Solution

The three points will be collinear if the vectors $\overrightarrow{AB}$ and $\overrightarrow{BC}$ have the same direction, or the opposite direction.

$\overrightarrow{AB} = (-8, 5)$
$\overrightarrow{BC} = (16, -10)$

Then $\overrightarrow{BC} = -2\overrightarrow{AB}$

$\overrightarrow{AB}$ and $\overrightarrow{BC}$ have the opposite direction, so the points A, B, and C must be collinear.

EXAMPLE 4

If $A(1, -5, 2)$ and $B(-3, 4, 4)$ are opposite vertices of parallelogram $OAPB$ and O is the origin, find the coordinates of P.

Solution

$$\overrightarrow{OP} = \overrightarrow{OB} + \overrightarrow{BP}$$

But $\overrightarrow{BP} = \overrightarrow{OA} = (1, -5, 2)$

Then $\overrightarrow{OP} = (-3, 4, 4) + (1, -5, 2)$
$$= (-2, -1, 6)$$

Therefore, point P has coordinates $(-2, -1, 6)$.

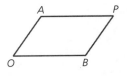

Exercise 2.2

Part A

1. In two dimensions, the unit vectors $\hat{i}$ and $\hat{j}$ have been chosen as the basis vectors in terms of which all other vectors in the plane are expressed.

   a. Consider the merits of this choice as opposed to using vectors that do not have unit magnitude.

   b. Consider the merits of this choice as opposed to using vectors that are not perpendicular.

2. Find a single vector equivalent to each expression below.

   a. $(2, -4) + (1, 7)$

   b. $5(1, 4)$

   c. $0(4, -5)$

   d. $(-6, 0) + 7(1, -1)$

   e. $(2, -1, 3) + (-2, 1, 3)$

   f. $2(1, 1, -4)$

   g. $(4, -1, 3) - (-2, 1, 3)$

   h. $2(-1, 1, 3) + 3(-2, 3, -1)$

   i. $2(0, 1, 0) + 5(0, 0, 1)$

   j. $-\frac{1}{2}(4, -6, 8) + \frac{3}{2}(4, -6, 8)$

   k. $5(0, -2, -4) - 4(3, 8, 0)$

   l. $-2(-3, 2, 4) + 5(3, 2, 8)$

3. Simplify each of the following expressions.

   a. $(2\hat{i} + 3\hat{j}) + 4(\hat{i} - \hat{j})$

   b. $3(\hat{i} - 2\hat{j} + 3\hat{k}) - 3(-\hat{i} + 4\hat{j} - 3\hat{k})$

   c. $-3(\hat{i} - \hat{k}) - (2\hat{i} + \hat{k})$

   d. $5(9\hat{i} - 7\hat{j}) - 5(-9\hat{i} + 7\hat{k})$

4. Given $\vec{a} = (2, -1, 4)$, $\vec{b} = (3, 8, -6)$, and $\vec{c} = (4, 2, 1)$, find a single vector equivalent to each of the following expressions.

   a. $2\vec{a} - \vec{b}$

   b. $\vec{a} - \vec{b}$

   c. $3\vec{a} - \vec{b} - 2\vec{c}$

   d. $\vec{a} + \vec{b} + 2\vec{c}$

   e. $-2\vec{a} + \vec{b} - \vec{c}$

   f. $4\vec{a} - 2\vec{b} + \vec{c}$

5. Given $\vec{x} = 2\hat{i} - \hat{j} + \hat{k}$ and $\vec{y} = 2\hat{j} + 4\hat{k}$, express each quantity in terms of $\hat{i}, \hat{j}$, and $\hat{k}$.

   a. $3\vec{x} + \vec{y}$

   b. $\vec{x} + \vec{y}$

   c. $\vec{x} - \vec{y}$

   d. $\vec{y} - \vec{x}$

6. If $\vec{a} = 3\hat{i} + 2\hat{j} - \hat{k}$ and $\vec{b} = -2\hat{i} + \hat{j}$, calculate each magnitude.

    a. $|\vec{a} + \vec{b}|$ b. $|\vec{a} - \vec{b}|$ c. $|2\vec{a} - 3\vec{b}|$

7. If $D(3, 4, 5)$ and $E(-2, 1, 5)$ are points in space, calculate each expression and state what it represents.

    a. $|\overrightarrow{OD}|$ b. $|\overrightarrow{OE}|$ c. $\overrightarrow{DE}$

    d. $|\overrightarrow{DE}|$ e. $\overrightarrow{ED}$ f. $|\overrightarrow{ED}|$

Part B

8. Using vectors, demonstrate that these points are collinear.

    a. $P(15, 10)$, $Q(6, 4)$, and $R(-12, -8)$

    b. $D(33, -5, 20)$, $E(6, 4, -16)$, and $F(9, 3, -12)$

9. For each set of points A, B, C, and D, determine whether $\overrightarrow{AB}$ is parallel to $\overrightarrow{CD}$ and whether $|\overrightarrow{AB}| = |\overrightarrow{CD}|$.

    a. $A(2, 0)$, $B(3, 6)$, $C(4, 1)$, $D(5, -5)$

    b. $A(0, 1, 0)$, $B(4, 0, 1)$, $C(5, 1, 2)$, $D(2, 3, 5)$

    c. $A(2, 4, 6)$, $B(3, 4, 1)$, $C(4, 1, 3)$, $D(5, 1, -2)$

10. If $PQRS$ is a parallelogram in a plane, where P is $(4, 2)$, Q is $(-6, 1)$, and S is $(-3, -4)$, find the coordinates of R.

11. If three vertices of a parallelogram in a plane are $(-5, 3)$, $(5, 2)$, and $(7, -8)$, determine all the possible coordinates of the fourth vertex.

12. If $\overrightarrow{OA}$, $\overrightarrow{OB}$, and $\overrightarrow{OC}$ are three edges of a **parallelepiped** where O is $(0, 0, 0)$, A is $(2, 4, -2)$, B is $(3, 6, 1)$, and C is $(4, 0, -1)$, find the coordinates of the other vertices of the parallelepiped.

13. A line segment has endpoints with position vectors $\overrightarrow{OA}_1$ and $\overrightarrow{OA}_2$. The midpoint of the line segment is the point with position vector

$$\overrightarrow{OM} = \frac{\overrightarrow{OA}_1 + \overrightarrow{OA}_2}{2}.$$

Find the position vector of the midpoint of the line segment from

    a. $A(-5, 2)$ to $B(13, 4)$ b. $C(3, 0)$ to $D(0, -7)$

    c. $E(6, 4, 2)$ to $F(-2, 8, -2)$ d. $G(0, 16, -5)$ to $H(9, -7, -1)$

14. a. Find x and y if $3(x, 1) - 2(2, y) = (2, 1)$.

    b. Find x, y, and z if $2(x, -1, 4) - 3(-4, y, 6) - \frac{1}{2}(4, -2, z) = (0, 0, 0)$.

15. Find the components of the unit vector with direction opposite to that of the vector from $X(7, 4, -2)$ to $Y(1, 2, 1)$.

16. a. Find the point on the y-axis that is equidistant from the points $(2, -1, 1)$ and $(0, 1, 3)$.

    b. Find a point not on the y-axis that is equidistant from the points $(2, -1, 1)$ and $(0, 1, 3)$.

17. a. Find the length of the median AM in the triangle ABC, for the points $A(2, \frac{3}{2}, -4)$, $B(3, -4, 2)$, and $C(1, 3, -7)$.

    b. Find the distance from A to the **centroid** of the triangle.

18. The centroid of the n points with position vectors OA_1, OA_2, ..., OA_n is the point with position vector
$$\overrightarrow{OC} = \frac{\overrightarrow{OA_1} + \overrightarrow{OA_2} + \ldots + \overrightarrow{OA_n}}{n}.$$
Find the centroid of each of the following sets of points.

    a. $A(1, 2)$, $B(4, -1)$, $C(-2, -2)$

    b. $I(1, 0, 0)$, $J(0, 1, 0)$, $K(0, 0, 1)$

    c. $A_1(3, -1)$, $A_2(1, 1)$, $A_3(7, 0)$, $A_4(4, 4)$

    d. $C(0, 0, 0)$, $I(1, 0, 0)$, $J(0, 1, 0)$, $K(0, 0, 1)$

19. The **centre of mass** of the masses m_1, m_2, ..., m_n at the points with position vectors $\overrightarrow{OA_1}$, $\overrightarrow{OA_2}$, ..., $\overrightarrow{OA_n}$, respectively, is the point with position vector
$$\overrightarrow{OG} = \frac{m_1\overrightarrow{OA_1} + m_2\overrightarrow{OA_2} + \ldots + m_n\overrightarrow{OA_n}}{m_1 + m_2 + \ldots + m_n}.$$

In some kinds of problems, a collection of masses can be replaced by a single large mass $M = m_1 + m_2 + \ldots + m_n$ located at the centre of mass, for the purposes of calculation. Calculate the centre of mass in each case.

    a. A mass of 2 units at $(0, 0)$, a mass of 3 units at $(4, 1)$, a mass of 5 units at $(-1, -7)$, and a mass of 1 unit at $(11, -9)$

    b. A mass of 1 unit at $(1, 4, -1)$, a mass of 3 units at $(-2, 0, 1)$, and a mass of 7 units at $(1, -3, 10)$

Section 2.3 — The Dot Product of Two Vectors

Certain applications of vectors in physics and geometry cannot be handled by the operatons of vector addition and scalar multiplication alone. Other, more sophisticated combinations of vectors are required. The **dot product** of two vectors is one of these combinations.

> The **dot product** of two vectors $\vec{u}$ and $\vec{v}$ is
> $$\vec{u} \cdot \vec{v} = |\vec{u}|\,|\vec{v}|\cos\theta,$$
> where θ is the angle between the two vectors.

Since the quantity $|\vec{u}|\,|\vec{v}|\cos\theta$ on the right is the product of three scalars, the dot product of two vectors is a scalar. For this reason, the dot product is also called the **scalar product**.

EXAMPLE 1

Find the dot product of $\vec{u}$ and $\vec{v}$ in each of the following cases, where θ is the angle between the vectors.

a. $|\vec{u}| = 7$, $|\vec{v}| = 12$, $\theta = 60°$ b. $|\vec{u}| = 20$, $|\vec{v}| = 3$, $\theta = \frac{5\pi}{6}$

         c. $|\vec{u}| = 24$, $|\vec{v}| = 9$, $\theta = 34°$

Solution

a. $\vec{u} \cdot \vec{v} = |\vec{u}|\,|\vec{v}|\cos 60°$ b. $\vec{u} \cdot \vec{v} = |\vec{u}|\,|\vec{v}|\cos\frac{5\pi}{6}$

      $= (7)(12)(0.5)$ $= (20)(3)\left(-\frac{\sqrt{3}}{2}\right)$

      $= 42$ $= -30\sqrt{3}$

               c. $\vec{u} \cdot \vec{v} = |\vec{u}|\,|\vec{v}|\cos 34°$

                    $= (24)(9)(0.8290)$

                    $\cong 179.1$

EXAMPLE 2

Prove that two non-zero vectors $\vec{u}$ and $\vec{v}$ are perpendicular, if and only if $\vec{u} \cdot \vec{v} = 0$.

Proof

The condition that $\vec{u} \cdot \vec{v} = 0$ is sufficient. Nothing else is needed to guarantee that the vectors are perpendicular, because

if $\vec{u} \cdot \vec{v} = 0$

then $|\vec{u}|\,|\vec{v}|\cos\theta = 0$

or $\cos\theta = 0$ (since the vectors are non-zero)

Therefore, $\theta = \pm 90°$,
which means that the vectors must be perpendicular.
The condition that $\vec{u} \cdot \vec{v} = 0$ is necessary, because

if $\qquad \vec{u} \cdot \vec{v} \neq 0$

then $\qquad |\vec{u}| |\vec{v}| \cos \theta \neq 0$,
which means that $\cos \theta$ cannot be zero.

Consequently, θ cannot be 90°.
So the vectors are perpendicular *only if* $\vec{u} \cdot \vec{v} = 0$.

The following properties of the dot product will be demonstrated in Exercise 2.3.

You can multiply by a scalar either $\qquad a(\vec{u} \cdot \vec{v}) = (a\vec{u}) \cdot \vec{v} = \vec{u} \cdot (a\vec{v})$
before or after taking the dot product.

You can expand a dot product of a vector $\qquad \vec{u} \cdot (\vec{v} + \vec{w}) = \vec{u} \cdot \vec{v} + \vec{u} \cdot \vec{w}$
with the sum of two other vectors as you would in ordinary multiplication.

The dot product of a vector $\vec{u}$ with itself $\qquad \vec{u} \cdot \vec{u} = |\vec{u}|^2$
is the square of the magnitude of the vector.

Dot products of the basis vectors $\hat{i}, \hat{j}$, and $\hat{k}$ are of particular importance.

Because they are unit vectors,	Because they are perpendicular,
$\hat{i} \cdot \hat{i} = 1$	$\hat{i} \cdot \hat{j} = \hat{j} \cdot \hat{i} = 0$
$\hat{j} \cdot \hat{j} = 1$	$\hat{j} \cdot \hat{k} = \hat{k} \cdot \hat{j} = 0$
$\hat{k} \cdot \hat{k} = 1$	$\hat{k} \cdot \hat{i} = \hat{i} \cdot \hat{k} = 0$

The dot product is 1 if the vectors are the same, and 0 if they are different.

These results are used to work out the dot product of two algebraic vectors, which, for vectors in space, proceeds in this manner:

If $\qquad \vec{u} = u_x\hat{i} + u_y\hat{k} + u_z\hat{k}$ and $\vec{v} = v_x\hat{i} + v_y\hat{j} + v_z\hat{k}$

then $\vec{u} \cdot \vec{v} = (u_x\hat{i} + u_y\hat{j} + u_z\hat{k}) \cdot (v_x\hat{i} + v_y\hat{j} + v_z\hat{k})$

$\qquad = u_xv_x(\hat{i} \cdot \hat{i}) + u_xv_y(\hat{i} \cdot \hat{j}) + u_xv_z(\hat{i} \cdot \hat{k})$

$\qquad + u_yv_x(\hat{j} \cdot \hat{i}) + u_yv_y(\hat{j} \cdot \hat{j}) + u_yv_z(\hat{j} \cdot \hat{k})$

$\qquad + u_zv_x(\hat{k} \cdot \hat{i}) + u_zv_y(\hat{k} \cdot \hat{j}) + u_zv_z(\hat{k} \cdot \hat{k})$

$\qquad = u_xv_x(1) + u_xv_y(0) + u_xv_z(0)$

$\qquad + u_yv_x(0) + u_yv_y(1) + u_yv_z(0)$

$\qquad + u_zv_x(0) + u_zv_y(0) + u_zv_z(1)$

$\qquad = u_xv_x + u_yv_y + u_zv_z$

EXAMPLE 3

Find the dot product of $\vec{u}$ and $\vec{v}$, where

a. $\vec{u} = (-5, 2)$ and $\vec{v} = (3, 4)$ b. $\vec{u} = (1, 0, 4)$ and $\vec{v} = (-2, 5, 8)$

Solution

$$\begin{aligned}\vec{u} \cdot \vec{v} &= (-5, 2) \cdot (3, 4) \\ &= (-5)(3) + (2)(4) \\ &= -15 + 8 \\ &= -7\end{aligned}$$

$$\begin{aligned}\vec{u} \cdot \vec{v} &= (1, 0, 4) \cdot (-2, 5, 8) \\ &= (1)(-2) + (0)(5) + (4)(8) \\ &= -2 + 0 + 32 \\ &= 30\end{aligned}$$

EXAMPLE 4

Find the angle θ between each of the following pairs of vectors.

a. $\vec{u} = (6, -5)$ and $\vec{v} = (-1, 3)$ b. $\vec{u} = (-3, 1, 2)$ and $\vec{v} = (5, -4, -1)$

Solution

Since $\vec{u} \cdot \vec{v} = |\vec{u}| \, |\vec{v}| \cos \theta$,

then $\cos \theta = \dfrac{\vec{u} \cdot \vec{v}}{|\vec{u}| \, |\vec{v}|}$.

a. $\cos \theta = \dfrac{(6, -5) \cdot (-1, -3)}{|(6, -5)| \, |(-1, -3)|}$

$ = \dfrac{(6)(-1) + (-5)(-3)}{\sqrt{(6)^2 + (-5)^2} \, \sqrt{(-1)^2 + (-3)^2}}$

$ = \dfrac{9}{\sqrt{61}\sqrt{10}} \cong 0.3644$

$\therefore \theta \cong 69°$

b. $\cos \theta = \dfrac{(-3, 1, 2) \cdot (5, -4, -1)}{|(-3, 1, 2)| \, |(5, -4, -1)|}$

$ = \dfrac{(-3)(5) + (1)(-4) + (2)(-1)}{\sqrt{(-3)^2 + (1)^2 + (2)^2} \, \sqrt{(5)^2 + (-4)^2 + (-1)^2}}$

$ = \dfrac{-21}{\sqrt{14}\sqrt{42}} = \dfrac{-\sqrt{3}}{2}$

$\therefore \theta = 150°$

Exercise 2.3

Part **A**

1. a. What is the dot product of two vectors if the angle between them is $0°$? $90°$? $180°$?

   b. What is the angle between two vectors if their dot product is positive? negative? zero?

2. Calculate the dot product $\vec{u} \cdot \vec{v}$, given the magnitudes of the two vectors and the angle θ between them.

   a. $|\vec{u}| = 3, |\vec{v}| = 4, \theta = 45°$ b. $|\vec{u}| = 6, |\vec{v}| = 5, \theta = 60°$

   c. $|\vec{u}| = 9, |\vec{v}| = 3, \theta = \frac{3\pi}{4}$ d. $|\vec{u}| = \frac{2}{3}, |\vec{v}| = \frac{9}{8}, \theta = 90°$

3. Examine each of the following pairs of vectors. State whether or not the vectors are perpendicular, then sketch each pair, and find their dot product.

   a. $\vec{a} = (4, 1), \vec{b} = (-1, 4)$ b. $\vec{c} = (5, 2), \vec{d} = (-5, -2)$

   c. $\vec{p} = (1, 0), \vec{q} = (0, -1)$ d. $\vec{u} = (7, 8), \vec{v} = (4, -7)$

4. Find the dot product of each of the following pairs of vectors and state which pairs are perpendicular.

   a. $\vec{a} = (-1, 3, 4), \vec{b} = (1, 3, -2)$ b. $\vec{x} = (-2, 2, 4), \vec{y} = (4, 1, -2)$

   c. $\vec{m} = (-5, 0, 0), \vec{n} = (0, -3, 0)$ d. $\vec{l} = (0, -3, 4), \vec{l} = (0, -3, 4)$

   e. $\vec{u} = (0, 5, 6), \vec{v} = (7, 0, 1)$ f. $\vec{c} = (8, -11, -5),$
   $\vec{d} = (-7, -11, -13)$

5. a. Find three vectors perpendicular to $(2, -3)$.

   b. How many unit vectors are perpendicular to a given vector in the xy-plane?

6. a. Find three non-collinear vectors perpendicular to $(2, -3, 1)$.

   b. How many unit vectors are perpendicular to a given vector in three dimensions?

7. Calculate, to four decimal places, the cosine of the angle between each of the following pairs of vectors. '

   a. $\vec{a} = (8, 9), \vec{b} = (9, 8)$ b. $\vec{c} = (1, -2, 3), \vec{d} = (4, 2, -1)$

Part B

8. Determine the angle between the following vectors.

   a. $\vec{a} = (3, 5), \vec{b} = (-4, 1)$

   b. $\vec{c} = (5, 6, -7), \vec{d} = (-2, 3, 1)$

   c. $\hat{i} = (1, 0, 0), \vec{m} = (1, 1, 1)$

   d. $\vec{p} = (2, -4, 5), \vec{q} = (0, 2, 3)$

9. Given $\vec{a} = (2, 3, 7)$ and $\vec{b} = (-4, y, -14)$,

   a. for what value of y are the vectors collinear?

   b. for what value of y are the vectors perpendicular?

10. Find any vector $\vec{w}$ that is perpendicular to both $\vec{u} = 3\hat{j} + 4\hat{k}$ and $\vec{v} = 2\hat{i}$.

11. If the vectors $\vec{a} = (2, 3, 4)$ and $\vec{b} = (10, y, z)$ are perpendicular, how must y and z be related?

12. For $\vec{u} = (1, 5, 8)$ and $\vec{v} = (-1, 3, -2)$, verify that

   a. $\vec{u} \cdot \vec{v} = \vec{v} \cdot \vec{u}$

   b. $\vec{u} \cdot \vec{u} = |\vec{u}|^2$ and $\vec{v} \cdot \vec{v} = |\vec{v}|^2$

   c. $(\vec{u} + \vec{v}) \cdot (\vec{u} - \vec{v}) = |\vec{u}|^2 - |\vec{v}|^2$

   d. $(\vec{u} + \vec{v}) \cdot (\vec{u} + \vec{v}) = |\vec{u}|^2 + 2\vec{u} \cdot \vec{v} + |\vec{v}|^2$

   e. $(2\vec{u}) \cdot \vec{v} = \vec{u} \cdot (2\vec{v}) = 2(\vec{u} \cdot \vec{v})$

13. If $\vec{u} = (2, 2, -1), \vec{v} = (3, -1, 0)$, and $\vec{w} = (1, 7, 8)$, verify that
    $\vec{u} \cdot (\vec{v} + \vec{w}) = \vec{u} \cdot \vec{v} + \vec{u} \cdot \vec{w}$.

14. Expand and simplify.

   a. $(4\hat{i} - \hat{j}) \cdot \hat{j}$

   b. $\hat{k} \cdot (\hat{j} - 3\hat{k})$

   c. $(\hat{i} - 4\hat{k}) \cdot (\hat{i} - 4\hat{k})$

15. Expand and simplify.

   a. $(3\vec{a} + 4\vec{b}) \cdot (5\vec{a} + 6\vec{b})$

   b. $(2\vec{a} - \vec{b}) \cdot (2\vec{a} + \vec{b})$

16. Find $(3\vec{a} + \vec{b}) \cdot (2\vec{b} - 4\vec{a})$, if $\vec{a} = -\hat{i} - 3\hat{j} + \hat{k}$ and $\vec{b} = 2\hat{i} + 4\hat{j} - 5\hat{k}$.

17. Two vectors $2\vec{a} + \vec{b}$ and $\vec{a} - 3\vec{b}$ are perpendicular. Find the angle between $\vec{a}$ and $\vec{b}$, if $|\vec{a}| = 2|\vec{b}|$.

18. Given $\hat{a}$ and $\hat{b}$ unit vectors,

   a. if the angle between them is 60°, calculate $(6\hat{a} + \hat{b}) \cdot (\hat{a} - 2\hat{b})$

   b. if $|\hat{a} + \hat{b}| = \sqrt{3}$, determine $(2\hat{a} - 5\hat{b}) \cdot (\hat{b} + 3\hat{a})$

19. The vectors $\vec{a} = 3\hat{i} - 4\hat{j} - \hat{k}$ and $\vec{b} = 2\hat{i} + 3\hat{j} - 6\hat{k}$ are the diagonals of a parallelogram. Show that this parallelogram is a rhombus, and determine the lengths of the sides and the angles between the sides.

20. a. If $\vec{a}$ and $\vec{b}$ are perpendicular, show that $|\vec{a}|^2 + |\vec{b}|^2 = |\vec{a} + \vec{b}|^2$. What is the usual name of this result?

    b. If $\vec{a}$ and $\vec{b}$ are not perpendicular, and $\vec{a} - \vec{b} = \vec{c}$, express $|\vec{c}|^2$ in terms of $\vec{a}$ and $\vec{b}$. What is the usual name of this result?

Part C

21. If the dot product of $\vec{a}$ and $\vec{b}$ is equal to the dot product of $\vec{a}$ and $\vec{c}$, this does not necessarily mean that $\vec{b}$ equals $\vec{c}$. Show why this is so

    a. by making an algebraic argument

    b. by drawing a geometrical diagram

22. Find a unit vector that is parallel to the xy-plane and perpendicular to the vector $4\hat{i} - 3\hat{j} + \hat{k}$.

23. Three vectors $\vec{x}$, $\vec{y}$, and $\vec{z}$ satisfy $\vec{x} + \vec{y} + \vec{z} = \vec{0}$. Calculate the value of $\vec{x} \cdot \vec{y} + \vec{y} \cdot \vec{z} + \vec{z} \cdot \vec{x}$, if $|\vec{x}| = 2$, $|\vec{y}| = 3$, and $|\vec{z}| = 4$.

24. A body diagonal of a cube is a line through the centre joining opposite vertices. Find the angles between the body diagonals of a cube.

25. a. Under what conditions is $(\vec{a} + \vec{b}) \cdot (\vec{a} - \vec{b}) = 0$? Give a geometrical interpretation of the vectors $\vec{a}$, $\vec{b}$, $\vec{a} + \vec{b}$, and $\vec{a} - \vec{b}$.

    b. Use the dot product to show that two vectors, which satisfy the equation $|\vec{u} + \vec{v}| = |\vec{u} - \vec{v}|$, must be perpendicular. How is the figure defined by $\vec{u}$ and $\vec{v}$ related to the figure defined by $\vec{a}$ and $\vec{b}$ of part **a**?

26. Prove that $|\vec{a} \cdot \vec{b}| \leq |\vec{a}| |\vec{b}|$. When does equality hold? Express this inequality in terms of components for vectors in two dimensions and for vectors in three dimensions. (This is known as the Cauchy-Schwarz Inequality.)

Section 2.4 — The Cross Product of Two Vectors

We have already defined the dot product of two vectors, which gives a scalar quantity. In this section we introduce a new product called the **cross product** or **vector product.** The cross product of two vectors $\vec{a}$ and $\vec{b}$ is a vector that is perpendicular to both $\vec{a}$ and $\vec{b}$. Hence, this cross product is defined only in three-dimensional space. The cross product is useful in many geometric and physical problems in three-dimensional space; it is used to help define torque and angular velocity in statics and dynamics, and it is also used in electromagnetic theory. We will use it to find vectors perpendicular to two given vectors.

Let $\vec{a} = (a_1, a_2, a_3)$ and $\vec{b} = (b_1, b_2, b_3)$ be two vectors in three-dimensional space. Let us find all the vectors $\vec{v} = (x, y, z)$ that are perpendicular to both $\vec{a}$ and $\vec{b}$.

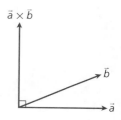

These vectors satisfy both
$\vec{a} \cdot \vec{v} = 0$ and $\vec{b} \cdot \vec{v} = 0$.
Hence,

$$a_1 x + a_2 y + a_3 z = 0 \qquad ①$$

$$b_1 x + b_2 y + b_3 z = 0 \qquad ②$$

We solve these two equations for x, y, and z. Multiply equation ① by b_3, and equation ② by a_3 to obtain

$$a_1 b_3 x + a_2 b_3 y + a_3 b_3 z = 0 \qquad ③$$

$$a_3 b_1 x + a_3 b_2 y + a_3 b_3 z = 0 \qquad ④$$

Now eliminate z by subtracting equation ③ from equation ④ to obtain

$$(a_3 b_1 - a_1 b_3)x + (a_3 b_2 - a_2 b_3)y = 0$$

This is equivalent to

$$\frac{x}{a_2 b_3 - a_3 b_2} = \frac{y}{a_3 b_1 - a_1 b_3}$$

Using a similar procedure, we eliminate x from the original equations to obtain

$$\frac{y}{a_3 b_1 - a_1 b_3} = \frac{z}{a_1 b_2 - a_2 b_1}$$

Let $y = k(a_3 b_1 - a_1 b_3)$, for some constant k.

Then $x = k(a_2 b_3 - a_3 b_2)$ and $z = k(a_1 b_2 - a_2 b_1)$.

Then the vector $\vec{v}$ perpendicular to both $\vec{a}$ and $\vec{b}$ is of the form
$\vec{v} = (x, y, z) = k(a_2 b_3 - a_3 b_2, a_3 b_1 - a_1 b_3, a_1 b_2 - a_2 b_1)$.

The cross product of $\vec{a}$ and $\vec{b}$ is chosen to be the vector of this form that has $k = 1$.

The **Cross Product** or **Vector Product** of $\vec{a} = (a_1, a_2, a_3)$ and $\vec{b} = (b_1, b_2, b_3)$ is the vector

$$\vec{a} \times \vec{b} = (a_2 b_3 - a_3 b_2, a_3 b_1 - a_1 b_3, a_1 b_2 - a_2 b_1).$$

This is a rather complicated expression to remember. It can be expressed as follows:

$$\vec{a} \times \vec{b} = \left(\begin{vmatrix} a_2 & a_3 \\ b_2 & b_3 \end{vmatrix}, \begin{vmatrix} a_3 & a_1 \\ b_3 & b_1 \end{vmatrix}, \begin{vmatrix} a_1 & a_2 \\ b_1 & b_2 \end{vmatrix} \right)$$

where $\begin{vmatrix} a & b \\ c & d \end{vmatrix} = ad - bc$

We showed above that any vector perpendicular to both the vectors $\vec{a}$ and $\vec{b}$ can be written as $k(\vec{a} \times \vec{b})$. This is one of the most useful properties of the cross product.

Finding a Vector Perpendicular to Two Vectors

If $\vec{a}$ and $\vec{b}$ are two non-collinear vectors in three-dimensional space, then every vector perpendicular to both $\vec{a}$ and $\vec{b}$ is of the form $k(\vec{a} \times \vec{b})$, for $k \in R$.

EXAMPLE 1   Find a vector perpendicular to both $(1, 3, 2)$ and $(4, -6, 7)$.

Solution
The cross product will be one such vector. From the definition of the cross product,
$$(1, 3, 2) \times (4, -6, 7) = (3(7) - 2(-6), 2(4) - 1(7), 1(-6) - 3(4))$$
$$= (33, 1, -18)$$

Hence, one vector perpendicular to $(1, 3, 2)$ and $(4, -6, 7)$ is $(33, 1, -18)$.

Hint: It is very easy to make errors in calculating a cross product. However, there is an easy check that should always be done after calculating any cross product. If $\vec{v} = \vec{a} \times \vec{b}$, you can always check that $\vec{a} \cdot \vec{v} = 0$ and $\vec{b} \cdot \vec{v} = 0$.

In our example,
$$(1, 3, 2) \cdot (33, 1, -18) = 1(33) + 3(1) + 2(-18)$$
$$= 0$$
$$(4, -6, 7) \cdot (33, 1, -18) = 4(33) - 6(1) + 7(-18)$$
$$= 0$$

Hence, $(33, 1, -18)$ is perpendicular to both $(1, 3, 2)$ and $(4, -6, 7)$.

The definition of cross product is motivated by the mechanical act of turning a bolt with a wrench, a process which involves vectors pointing in three different directions.

If, for instance, a bolt with a right-hand thread is turned clockwise, it moves down along the axis of rotation in a direction perpendicular to both the wrench handle and the turning force. This gives a definition for the magnitude of the cross-product vector.

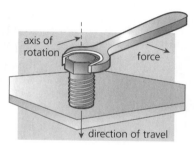

The magnitude of the cross product of two vectors $\vec{a}$ and $\vec{b}$ is
$$|\vec{a} \times \vec{b}| = |\vec{a}| \, |\vec{b}| \sin \theta$$
where θ is the angle between the vectors, $0 \le \theta \le 180°$.

We will prove that $|\vec{a} \times \vec{b}| = |\vec{a}| \, |\vec{b}| \sin \theta$.

Let $\vec{a} = (a_1, a_2, a_3)$ and $\vec{b} = (b_1, b_2, b_3)$ so that
$$\vec{a} \times \vec{b} = (a_2b_3 - a_3b_2, \; a_3b_1 - a_1b_3, \; a_1b_2 - a_2b_1)$$

Then $|\vec{a} \times \vec{b}|^2 = (a_2b_3 - a_3b_2)^2 + (a_3b_1 - a_1b_3)^2 + (a_1b_2 - a_2b_1)^2$

By adding and subtracting $(a_1b_1)^2 + (a_2b_2)^2 + (a_3b_3)^2$ to the right side this can be rewritten as

$$
\begin{aligned}
|\vec{a} \times \vec{b}|^2 &= (a_1{}^2 + a_2{}^2 + a_3{}^2)(b_1{}^2 + b_2{}^2 + b_3{}^2) - (a_1b_1 + a_2b_2 + a_3b_3)^2 \\
&= |\vec{a}|^2 |\vec{b}|^2 - (\vec{a} \cdot \vec{b})^2 \\
&= |\vec{a}|^2 |\vec{b}|^2 - (|\vec{a}| \, |\vec{b}| \cos \theta)^2 \\
&= |\vec{a}|^2 |\vec{b}|^2 (1 - \cos^2 \theta) \\
&= |\vec{a}|^2 |\vec{b}|^2 \sin^2 \theta
\end{aligned}
$$

Since $0 \le \theta \le 180°$, $\sin \theta \ge 0$, and so $|\vec{a} \times \vec{b}| = |\vec{a}| \, |\vec{b}| \sin \theta$.

There are two vectors perpendicular to $\vec{a}$ and $\vec{b}$ with the same magnitude but opposite in direction. The choice of direction of the cross product is such that $\vec{a}$, $\vec{b}$, and $\vec{a} \times \vec{b}$ form a right-handed system. Hence, we have the following geometric description of the cross product.

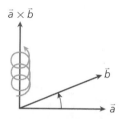

The cross product of the vectors $\vec{a}$ and $\vec{b}$ in three-dimensional space is the vector whose magnitude is $|\vec{a}| \, |\vec{b}| \sin \theta$ and whose direction is perpendicular to $\vec{a}$ and $\vec{b}$, such that $\vec{a}$, $\vec{b}$, and $\vec{a} \times \vec{b}$ form a right-handed system.

The direction of the cross product $\vec{u} \times \vec{v}$ of two vectors drawn in a plane can be found by placing your right hand on the diagram so that your fingers curl in the direction of rotation from $\vec{u}$ to $\vec{v}$, through an angle less than 180°. Your thumb points in the direction of $\vec{u} \times \vec{v}$. Try it on the two diagrams below.

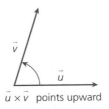

$\vec{u} \times \vec{v}$ points upward

$\vec{u} \times \vec{v}$ points downward

EXAMPLE 2

If $|\vec{u}| = 4$ and $|\vec{v}| = 10$ and the angle θ between $\vec{u}$ and $\vec{v}$ is 60°, find $|\vec{u} \times \vec{v}|$.

Solution

$$|\vec{u} \times \vec{v}| = |\vec{u}| \, |\vec{v}| \, \sin 60°$$
$$= (4)(10)\left(\frac{\sqrt{3}}{2}\right)$$
$$\cong 34.6$$

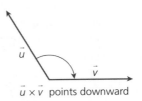

10

60°

4

direction up

Then $\vec{u} \times \vec{v}$ has magnitude 34.6 and a direction vertically up from the plane defined by $\vec{u}$ and $\vec{v}$.

EXAMPLE 3

Find the cross product of $\vec{u} = 6\hat{i} - 2\hat{j} - 3\hat{k}$ and $\vec{v} = 5\hat{i} + \hat{j} - 4\hat{k}$.

Solution

By direct substitution,
$$\vec{u} \times \vec{v} = [(-2)(-4) - (-3)(1)]\hat{i} + [(-3)(5) - (6)(-4)]\hat{j} + [(6)(1) - (-2)(5)]\hat{k}$$
$$= [(8) - (-3)]\hat{i} + [(-15) - (-24)]\hat{j} + [(6) - (-10)]\hat{k}$$
$$= 11\hat{i} + 9\hat{j} + 16\hat{k}$$

or
$$\vec{u} \times \vec{v} = \begin{vmatrix} -2 & -3 \\ 1 & -4 \end{vmatrix} \hat{i} + \begin{vmatrix} -3 & 6 \\ -4 & 5 \end{vmatrix} \hat{j} + \begin{vmatrix} 6 & -2 \\ 5 & 1 \end{vmatrix} \hat{k}$$
$$= 11\hat{i} + 9\hat{j} + 16\hat{k}$$

Properties of the Cross Product

Let $\vec{a}$, $\vec{b}$, and $\vec{c}$ be vectors in three-dimensional space and let $t \in R$.

$\vec{a} \times \vec{b} = -(\vec{b} \times \vec{a})$ (Anti-commutative Law)

$\vec{a} \times (\vec{b} + \vec{c}) = (\vec{a} \times \vec{b}) + (\vec{a} \times \vec{c})$ (Distributive Law)

$k(\vec{a} \times \vec{b}) = (k\vec{a}) \times \vec{b} = \vec{a} \times (k\vec{b})$

These properties can be checked by using the definition of the cross product. Notice that the first property means that the cross product is not commutative. For example, $\vec{i} \times \vec{j} = \vec{k}$, but $\vec{j} \times \vec{i} = -\vec{k}$.

Since the result of a cross product is a vector, you may form the dot product or the cross product of this vector with a third vector. The quantity $(\vec{u} \times \vec{v}) \bullet \vec{w}$ is known as the triple scalar product of three vectors because it is a scalar quantity. The brackets are not really needed to specify the order of operations because $\vec{u} \times (\vec{v} \bullet \vec{w})$ is meaningless. (Why?) The quantity $(\vec{u} \times \vec{v}) \times \vec{w}$ is a vector and is called the triple vector product. Brackets are required in this expression to specify the order of operations. Both of these quantities arise in the application of vectors to physical and geometrical problems. Some of their properties are investigated in the exercises.

Exercise 2.4

Part A

1. If $\vec{w} = \vec{u} \times \vec{v}$, explain why $\vec{w} \bullet \vec{u}$, $\vec{w} \bullet \vec{v}$, and $\vec{w} \bullet (a\vec{u} + b\vec{v})$ are all zero.

2. Find $|\vec{u} \times \vec{v}|$ for each of the following pairs of vectors. State whether $\vec{u} \times \vec{v}$ is directed into or out of the page.

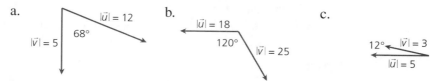

a.
$|\vec{u}| = 12$
$68°$
$|\vec{v}| = 5$

b.
$|\vec{u}| = 18$
$120°$
$|\vec{v}| = 25$

c.
$12°$ $|\vec{v}| = 3$
$|\vec{u}| = 5$

3. State whether the following expressions are vectors, scalars, or meaningless.

   a. $\vec{a} \bullet (\vec{b} \times \vec{c})$
   b. $(\vec{a} \bullet \vec{b}) \times (\vec{b} \bullet \vec{c})$
   c. $(\vec{a} + \vec{b}) \bullet \vec{c}$
   d. $\vec{a} \times (\vec{b} \bullet \vec{c})$
   e. $(\vec{a} \times \vec{b}) \bullet (\vec{b} \times \vec{c})$
   f. $(\vec{a} + \vec{b}) \times \vec{c}$
   g. $\vec{a} \bullet (\vec{b} \bullet \vec{c})$
   h. $(\vec{a} \times \vec{b}) + (\vec{b} \times \vec{c})$
   i. $(\vec{a} \times \vec{b}) - \vec{c}$
   j. $\vec{a} \times (\vec{b} \times \vec{c})$
   k. $(\vec{a} \bullet \vec{b}) + (\vec{b} \bullet \vec{c})$
   l. $(\vec{a} \bullet \vec{b}) - \vec{c}$

4. Use the cross product to find a vector perpendicular to each of the following pairs of vectors. Check your answer using the dot product.

   a. $(4, 0, 0)$ and $(0, 0, 4)$
   b. $(1, 2, 1)$ and $(6, 0, 6)$
   c. $(2, -1, 3)$ and $(1, 4, -2)$
   d. $(0, 2, -5)$ and $(-4, 9, 0)$

Part B

5. Find a unit vector perpendicular to $\vec{a} = (4, -3, 1)$ and $\vec{b} = (2, 3, -1)$.

6. Find two vectors perpendicular to both (3, −6, 3) and (−2, 4, 2).

7. Express the unit vectors $\hat{i}, \hat{j}$, and $\hat{k}$ as ordered triples and show that
   a. $\hat{i} \times \hat{j} = \hat{k}$
   b. $\hat{k} \times \hat{j} = -\hat{i}$

8. Using components, show that
   a. $\vec{u} \times \vec{v} = -\vec{v} \times \vec{u}$ for any vectors $\vec{u}$ and $\vec{v}$
   b. $\vec{u} \times \vec{v} = \vec{0}$, if $\vec{u}$ and $\vec{v}$ are collinear

9. Prove that $|\vec{a} \times \vec{b}| = \sqrt{(\vec{a} \cdot \vec{a})(\vec{b} \cdot \vec{b}) - (\vec{a} \cdot \vec{b})^2}$.

10. Given $\vec{a} = (2, 1, 0)$, $\vec{b} = (-1, 0, 3)$, and $\vec{c} = (4, -1, 1)$, calculate the following triple scalar and triple vector products.
    a. $\vec{a} \times \vec{b} \cdot \vec{c}$
    b. $\vec{b} \times \vec{c} \cdot \vec{a}$
    c. $\vec{c} \times \vec{a} \cdot \vec{b}$
    d. $(\vec{a} \times \vec{b}) \times \vec{c}$
    e. $(\vec{b} \times \vec{c}) \times \vec{a}$
    f. $(\vec{c} \times \vec{a}) \times \vec{b}$

11. By choosing $\vec{u} = \vec{v}$, show that $\vec{u} \times (\vec{v} \times \vec{w}) \neq (\vec{u} \times \vec{v}) \times \vec{w}$. This means that, in general, the cross product is not associative.

12. Given two non-collinear vectors $\vec{a}$ and $\vec{b}$, show that $\vec{a}$, $\vec{a} \times \vec{b}$, and $(\vec{a} \times \vec{b}) \times \vec{a}$ are mutually perpendicular.

13. Prove that the triple scalar product of the vectors $\vec{u}, \vec{v}$, and $\vec{w}$ has the property that $\vec{u} \cdot (\vec{v} \times \vec{w}) = (\vec{u} \times \vec{v}) \cdot \vec{w}$. Carry out the proof by expressing both sides of the equation in terms of components of the vectors.

Part C

14. If the cross product of $\vec{a}$ and $\vec{b}$ is equal to the cross product of $\vec{a}$ and $\vec{c}$, this does not necessarily mean that $\vec{b}$ equals $\vec{c}$. Show why this is so
    a. by making an algebraic argument
    b. by drawing a geometrical diagram

15. a. If $\vec{a} = (1, 3, -1)$, $\vec{b} = (2, 1, 5)$, $\vec{v} = (-3, y, z)$, and $\vec{a} \times \vec{v} = \vec{b}$, find y and z.
    b. Find *another* vector $\vec{v}$ for which $\vec{a} \times \vec{v} = \vec{b}$.
    c. Explain why there are infinitely many vectors $\vec{v}$ for which $\vec{a} \times \vec{v} = \vec{b}$.

Section 2.5 — Applications of Dot and Cross Products

In this section, we will apply the dot product and the cross product to problems in geometry and physics.

Projections

Mathematically, a **projection** is formed by *dropping* a perpendicular from each of the points of an object onto a line or plane. The shadow of an object, in certain circumstances, is a physical example of a projection.

The projection of one vector onto another can be pictured as follows. In the given diagram, where $\vec{u} = \overrightarrow{OA}$ and $\vec{v} = \overrightarrow{OB}$, the projection of $\vec{u}$ onto $\vec{v}$ is the vector $\overrightarrow{ON}$. There is no special symbol for a projection. In this text, we use the notation

$$\overrightarrow{ON} = \text{Proj}(\vec{u} \text{ onto } \vec{v}).$$

The magnitude of $\overrightarrow{ON}$ is given by

$$\left| \, |\vec{u}| \cos \theta \, \right| = \frac{\left| \, |\vec{u}| \cos \theta \, \right| |\vec{v}|}{|\vec{v}|}$$

$$= \frac{|\vec{u}| \, |\vec{v}| \cos \theta}{|\vec{v}|}$$

$$= \frac{|\vec{u} \cdot \vec{v}|}{|\vec{v}|}$$

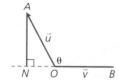

As you can see from the given diagrams, the direction of $\overrightarrow{ON}$ is the same as the direction of $\vec{v}$ when θ is acute, and opposite to $\vec{v}$ when θ is obtuse. The sign of $\cos \theta$ in the dot product takes care of both possibilities. Therefore,

> The **projection** of $\vec{u}$ onto $\vec{v}$ is
>
> $$\text{Proj}(\vec{u} \text{ onto } \vec{v}) = \frac{(\vec{u} \cdot \vec{v})\vec{v}}{|\vec{v}|^2}.$$
>
> Its magnitude is $\dfrac{|\vec{u} \cdot \vec{v}|}{|\vec{v}|}.$

EXAMPLE 1

Find the projection of $\vec{u} = (5, 6, -3)$ onto $\vec{v} = (1, 4, 5)$.

Solution

First, we calculate $\vec{u} \bullet \vec{v}$ and $|\vec{v}|^2$.

$$\vec{u} \bullet \vec{v} = (5, 6, -3) \bullet (1, 4, 5) = 14$$

$$|\vec{v}|^2 = 1^2 + 4^2 + 5^2 = 42$$

Therefore, $\text{Proj}(\vec{u} \text{ onto } \vec{v})$

$$= \frac{(\vec{u} \bullet \vec{v})\vec{v}}{|\vec{v}|^2}$$

$$= \frac{14(1, 4, 5)}{42}$$

$$= \left(\frac{1}{3}, \frac{4}{3}, \frac{5}{3} \right)$$

Area of a Parallelogram

The area of a parallelogram is the product of its base and its height: $A = bh$. The base of the parallelogram in the given diagram is $|\vec{v}|$ and its height is equal to $|\vec{u}| \sin \theta$. Its area is therefore $A = |\vec{v}| |\vec{u}| \sin \theta$, which you will recognize to be the magnitude of the cross product of the two vectors $\vec{u}$ and $\vec{v}$ that make up the sides of the parallelogram.

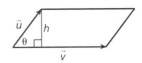

> The **area of a parallelogram** having $\vec{u}$ and $\vec{v}$ as sides is
>
> $A = |\vec{u} \times \vec{v}|$.

EXAMPLE 2

Find the area of the triangle with vertices $P(7, 2, -5)$, $Q(9, -1, -6)$, and $R(7, 3, -3)$.

Solution

Start by finding the vectors that form two sides of this triangle. The area of the triangle is half the area of the parallelogram having these vectors as sides.

Vectors
$$\vec{PQ} = (2, -3, -1)$$
$$\vec{PR} = (0, 1, 2)$$

Cross product $\quad \vec{PQ} \times \vec{PR} = (2, -3, -1) \times (0, 1, 2) = (-5, -4, 2)$

Magnitude $|(-5, -4, 2)| = \sqrt{(-5)^2 + (-4)^2 + (2)^2} = \sqrt{45}$

The area of the triangle is therefore $\dfrac{\sqrt{45}}{2}$ or $\dfrac{3\sqrt{5}}{2}$.

Volume of a Parallelepiped

A **parallelepiped** is a box-like solid, the opposite faces of which are parallel and congruent parallelograms. Its edges are three non-coplanar vectors $\vec{a}$, $\vec{b}$, and $\vec{c}$.

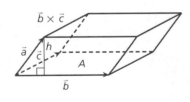

The volume V of a parallelepiped, like that of a cylinder, is the area of the base A times the height h, which is measured along a line perpendicular to the base. The area of the base is the area of the parallelogram determined by the vectors $\vec{b}$ and $\vec{c}$:

$$A = |\vec{b} \times \vec{c}|$$

The height is the magnitude of the projection of $\vec{a}$ onto the normal to the base, which is in the direction of $\vec{b} \times \vec{c}$:

$$h = |\text{Proj}(\vec{a} \text{ onto } \vec{b} \times \vec{c})|$$
$$= \frac{|\vec{a} \cdot (\vec{b} \times \vec{c})|}{|\vec{b} \times \vec{c}|}$$

The volume is therefore

$$V = Ah$$
$$= |\vec{b} \times \vec{c}| \frac{|\vec{a} \cdot (\vec{b} \times \vec{c})|}{|\vec{b} \times \vec{c}|}$$
$$= |\vec{a} \cdot (\vec{b} \times \vec{c})|$$

In other words, the volume of the parallelepiped is the magnitude of the triple scalar product of the three vectors that make up its edges. Since the volume is a constant, independent of which face is chosen as the base, this result illustrates an important property of the triple scalar product. If $\vec{a} \cdot \vec{b} \times \vec{c} = t$, and t is a constant, then $\vec{b} \cdot \vec{c} \times \vec{a} = \vec{c} \cdot \vec{a} \times \vec{b} = t$, and $\vec{a} \cdot \vec{c} \times \vec{b} = \vec{c} \cdot \vec{b} \times \vec{a} = \vec{b} \cdot \vec{a} \times \vec{c} = -t$.

Work

In everyday life, the word *work* is applied to any form of activity that requires physical exertion or mental effort. In physics, the word *work* has a much narrower meaning: **work** is done whenever a force acting on an object causes a displacement of the object from one position to another. For instance, work is done by the force of gravity when an object falls because the force displaces the object from a higher to a lower position. While it might seem like *hard work* to hold a heavy object, if you do not move, you are doing no work.

The **work** done by a force is defined as the dot product

$$W = \vec{F} \cdot \vec{d}$$
$$= |\vec{F}| \, |\vec{d}| \cos \theta$$

where $\vec{F}$ is the force acting on an object,
$\vec{d}$ is the displacement caused by the force,
and θ is the angle between the force and displacement vectors.

Work is a scalar quantity. The unit of work is a *joule* (J).

EXAMPLE 3

a. A 25-kg box is located 8 m up a ramp inclined at an angle of 18° to the horizontal. Determine the work done by the force of gravity as the box slides to the bottom of the ramp.

b. Determine the minimum force, acting at an angle of 40° to the horizontal, required to slide the box back up the ramp. (Ignore friction.)

Solution

a. The angle between the displacement down the ramp and the force of gravity is the difference $90° - 18° = 72°$. The force of gravity is $\vec{F}_g = (25 \text{ kg})(9.8 \text{ m/s}^2) = 245 \text{ N}$. Therefore, the work done by gravity would be

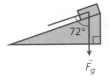

$$W = \vec{F}_g \bullet \vec{d}$$
$$= (245)(8) \cos 72°$$
$$\cong 606 \text{ J}$$

b. The gravitational force acting down the ramp is $245 \cos 72°$.

The applied force acting up the ramp is $|\vec{F}_a| \cos 22°$.

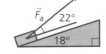

Then $|\vec{F}_a| = \dfrac{245 \cos 72°}{\cos 22°}$

$$\doteq 81.7$$

The force must exceed 81.7 N.

Torque

Sometimes, instead of causing a change in position, a force causes an object to turn; that is, the force causes an angular rather than a linear displacement. This turning effect of a force is called **torque.**

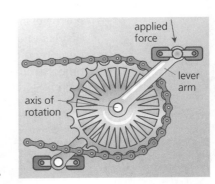

The force exerted by a cyclist on a bicycle pedal, for example, turns the pedal about an axis. The distance along the shaft of the pedal from the axis of rotation to the point at which the force is applied is known as the **lever arm.** The maximum turning effect occurs when the force is perpendicular to the lever arm.

The **torque** caused by a force is defined as the cross product

$$\vec{T} = \vec{r} \times \vec{F}$$
$$= |\vec{r}| \, |\vec{F}| \, \sin \theta \, \hat{n}$$

where $\vec{F}$ is the applied force,
$\vec{r}$ is the vector determined by the lever arm acting from the axis
   of rotation,
θ is the angle between the force and the lever arm,
and $\hat{n}$ is a unit vector perpendicular to both $\vec{r}$ and $\vec{F}$.

Torque is a vector quantity. It is measured in units of newton metres (N-m).

EXAMPLE 4

Find the torque produced by a cyclist exerting a force of 115 N on a pedal in the position shown in the diagram, if the shaft of the pedal is 16 cm long.

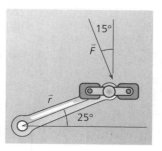

Solution
As with any problem involving forces, the first step is to change the picture showing where the forces act into a vector diagram. In this case, that means placing the vectors tail to tail and determining the angle between them. This angle, as you can see, is 100°. Therefore, the magnitude of the torque is

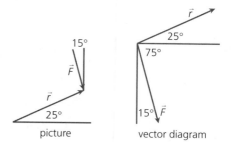

$$|\vec{T}| = |\vec{r}| \, |\vec{F}| \, \sin \theta$$
$$= (0.16)(115)\sin 100°$$
$$\cong 18.1 \text{ N-m}$$

The direction of the torque vector is into the page, as determined by the right-hand rule.

Part A

1. For each of the following, find the projection of $\vec{u}$ onto $\vec{v}$ and calculate its magnitude.

    a. $\vec{u} = (2, 5)$, $\vec{v} = (6, 4)$

    b. $\vec{u} = (-2, 4)$, $\vec{v} = (-3, 2)$

    c. $\vec{u} = (3, 6, -2)$, $\vec{v} = (-4, 3, 8)$

    d. $\vec{u} = (27, 11, -4)$, $\vec{v} = (0, 0, 8)$

2. a. If $\vec{u}$ and $\vec{v}$ are non-zero vectors, but Proj($\vec{u}$ onto $\vec{v}$) = $\vec{0}$, what conclusion can be drawn?

    b. If Proj($\vec{u}$ onto $\vec{v}$) = $\vec{0}$, does it follow that Proj($\vec{v}$ onto $\vec{u}$) = $\vec{0}$? Explain.

3. Find the projection of $\vec{u} = (2, 3, -4)$ onto each of the coordinate axes.

4. Find the projection of $\vec{PQ}$ onto each of the coordinate axes, where P is the point $(2, 3, 5)$ and Q is the point $(-1, 2, 5)$.

Part B

5. a. Find the projection of an edge of a unit cube onto one of its body diagonals.

    b. Find the projection of a body diagonal of a unit cube onto one of its edges.

6. Calculate the area of the parallelogram with sides consisting of the vectors

    a. $\vec{a} = (1, 2, -2)$ and $\vec{b} = (-1, 3, 0)$

    b. $\vec{c} = (-6, 4, -12)$ and $\vec{d} = (9, -6, 18)$

7. Find the area of the triangle with the given vertices.

    a. $(7, 3, 4)$, $(1, 0, 6)$, and $(4, 5, -2)$ b. $(1, 0, 0)$, $(0, 1, 0)$, and $(0, 0, 1)$

8. Find the volume of the parallelepiped determined by the vectors $\vec{a} = (2, -5, -1)$, $\vec{b} = (4, 0, 1)$, and $\vec{c} = (3, -1, -1)$.

9. For each of the following, calculate the work done by a force $\vec{F}$ that causes a displacement $\vec{d}$, if the angle between the force and the displacement is θ.

    a. $|\vec{F}| = 220\ N$, $|\vec{d}| = 15\ m$, $\theta = 49°$

    b. $|\vec{F}| = 4.3\ N$, $|\vec{d}| = 2.6\ m$, $\theta = 85°$

    c. $|\vec{F}| = 14\ N$, $|\vec{d}| = 6\ m$, $\theta = 110°$

    d. $|\vec{F}| = 4000\ kN$, $|\vec{d}| = 5\ km$, $\theta = 90°$

10. How much work is done in sliding a refrigerator 1.5 m across a kitchen floor against a frictional force of 150 N?

11. How much work is done by gravity in causing a 30-kg rock to tumble 40 m down a slope at an angle of 52° to the vertical?

12. A pedicab is pulled a distance of 300 m by a force of 110 N applied at an angle of 6° to the roadway. Calculate the work done.

13. How much work is done against gravity by a workman carrying an 8-kg sheet of plywood up a 3-m ramp inclined at an angle of 20° to the horizontal?

14. A 35-kg trunk is dragged 10 m up a ramp inclined at an angle of 12° to the horizontal by a force of 90 N applied at an angle of 20° to the ramp. At the top of the ramp, the trunk is dragged horizontally another 15 m by the same force. Find the total work done.

15. For each of the following, find the work done by a force $\vec{F}$ that causes a displacement $\vec{d}$.
   a. $\vec{F} = 2\hat{i}$, $\vec{d} = 5\hat{i} + 6\hat{j}$
   b. $\vec{F} = 4\hat{i} + \hat{j}, \vec{d} = 3\hat{i} + 10\hat{j}$
   c. $\vec{F} = (800, 600), \vec{d} = (20, 50)$
   d. $\vec{F} = 12\hat{i} - 5\hat{j} + 6\hat{k}, \vec{d} = -2\hat{i} + 8\hat{j} - 4\hat{k}$

16. If a 10-N force, acting in the direction of the vector $(1, 1)$, moves an object from $P(-2, 1)$ to $Q(5, 6)$, calculate the work done. The distance is in metres.

17. Find the work done by a 30-N force acting in the direction of the vector $(-2, 1, 5)$, which moves an object from $A(2, 1, 5)$ to $B(3, -1, 2)$. The distance is in metres.

18. A 50-N force is applied to the end of a 20-cm wrench and makes an angle of 30° with the handle of the wrench.
   a. What is the torque on a bolt at the other end of the wrench?
   b. What is the maximum torque that can be exerted by a 50-N force on this wrench and how can it be achieved?

Part C

19. Under what circumstances is
   a. $\text{Proj}(\vec{u} \text{ onto } \vec{v}) = \text{Proj}(\vec{v} \text{ onto } \vec{u})$?
   b. $|\text{Proj}(\vec{u} \text{ onto } \vec{v})| = |\text{Proj}(\vec{v} \text{ onto } \vec{u})|$?

Review Exercise

1. Express each vector in the form $a\hat{i} + b\hat{j} + c\hat{k}$.

   a. $(1, 3, 2)$ b. $(1, 0, 5)$ c. $(-6, -8, 11)$ d. $(9, -6, 2)$

2. Express each vector in the form (a, b, c).

   a. $3\hat{i} - 2\hat{j} + 7\hat{k}$ b. $-9\hat{i} + 3\hat{j} + 14k$

   c. $\hat{i} + \hat{j}$ d. $2\hat{i} - 9\hat{k}$

3. a. Find the dot product of the two vectors $\vec{u}$ and $\vec{v}$ where

   $\vec{u} = (3, -4, 1), \vec{v} = (2, 1, -5)$.

   b. Find the angle between $\vec{u}$ and $\vec{v}$.

4. Find a vector that is perpendicular to both of the vectors $\vec{a} = (1, 2, 4)$ and $\vec{b} = (0, 3, -2)$.

5. Expand $(\vec{a} + \vec{b}) \cdot (\vec{a} - \vec{b})$. Write your answer in the simplest form.

6. Expand $(\vec{a} + \vec{b}) \cdot (\vec{c} + \vec{d})$.

7. The cosine of the angle between $\vec{a}$ and $\vec{b}$ is $\frac{4}{21}$. Find p,

   if $\vec{a} = 6\hat{i} + 3\hat{j} - 2\hat{k}$ and $\vec{b} = -2\hat{i} + p\hat{j} - 4\hat{k}$.

8. Find λ so that the vectors $\hat{i} + \hat{j} + \hat{k}$ and $\lambda^2\hat{i} - 2\lambda\hat{j} + \hat{k}$ are perpendicular.

9. Calculate the dot product of $4\vec{x} - \vec{y}$ and $2\vec{x} + 3\vec{y}$, if $|\vec{x}| = 3$, $|\vec{y}| = 4$, and the angle between $\vec{x}$ and $\vec{y}$ is $60°$.

10. A vector $\vec{u}$ with direction angles α_1, β_1, and γ_1 is perpendicular to a vector $\vec{v}$ with direction angles α_2, β_2, and γ_2. Prove that

    $\cos \alpha_1 \cos \alpha_2 + \cos \beta_1 \cos \beta_2 + \cos \gamma_1 \cos \gamma_2 = 0$.

11. Show that $\vec{x} \cdot \vec{y} = \frac{1}{2}(|\vec{x} + \vec{y}^2| - |\vec{x}|^2 - |\vec{y}|^2)$.

12. A triangle has vertices $A(-1, 3, 4)$, $B(3, -1, 1)$, and $C(5, 1, 1)$.

    a. Show that the triangle is right-angled.

    b. Calculate the area of triangle ABC.

c. Calculate the perimeter of triangle ABC.

d. Determine the fourth vertex needed to complete a rectangle.

13. Find the projection of $\vec{u} = (17, -3, 8)$

   a. onto each of the coordinate axes

   b. onto each of the coordinate planes

14. Use the cross product to find the area of the triangle whose vertices all lie in the xy-plane at coordinates $A(-7, 3, 0)$, $B(3, 1, 0)$ and $C(2, -6, 0)$.

15. A regular tetrahedron has one vertex at the origin, one vertex at $(0, 1, 0)$, and one vertex, with a positive x-coordinate, on the xy-plane.

   a. Find the coordinates of the four vertices.

   b. Find the coordinates of the centroid of the tetrahedron.

   c. How far is the centroid from each vertex?

16. For any vectors $\vec{a}$, $\vec{b}$ and $\vec{c}$, show that

   a. $(\vec{a} \times \vec{b}) \times \vec{c}$ lies in the plane of $\vec{a}$ and $\vec{b}$

   b. $(\vec{a} \times \vec{b}) \times \vec{c} = (\vec{a} \cdot \vec{c})\vec{b} - (\vec{b} \cdot \vec{c})\vec{a}$

17. Find the volume of the tetrahedron with vertices $(1, 1, 2)$, $(3, -4, 6)$, $(-7, 0, -1)$, and $(-1, 5, 8)$.

The geometry of a molecule is one factor in determining its properties. Bond angles are one quantitative aspect of molecular geometry. The term *valence electrons* refers to those electrons that are most weakly bound to an atom and are, therefore, involved in the formation of chemical bonds. A theory about the relationship between valence electrons and angles of chemical bonds was proposed in 1939 by N. V. Sidgwick and H. M. Powell. They theorized that bonds tend to keep as far apart as possible.

Investigate and Apply

Methane (CH_4) consists of four hydrogen atoms bonded to a single carbon atom. The hydrogen atoms are all 1.095×10^{-11} metres from the carbon atom, and they are distributed evenly in three dimensions to be as far apart as possible. The resulting shape for the four hydrogen atoms is called a regular tetrahedron. The carbon atom is located at the centre of the regular tetrahedron. Other regular tetrahedral molecules include SiH_4, GeH_4, and SnH_4. They are different sizes, but they all have the hydrogen atoms evenly distributed.

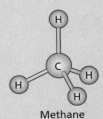

Methane

One way to define a regular tetrahedron in three-dimensional space is to connect the four vertices at (0, 0, 0), (1, 1, 0), (1, 0, 1), and (0, 1, 1).

1. Verify that the four points listed are all equidistant from each other.
2. Draw a three-dimensional coordinate system and then draw the vertices and edges of the given regular tetrahedron.
3. Find the centre of the given regular tetrahedron. *Hint:* Its three coordinates are all equal, and it is equidistant from each vertex.
4. Use dot product methods to find the angle formed between any two vectors extending from the centre of the regular tetrahedron to two of its vertices.
5. Why is your answer to question **4** the bond angle in CH_4, SiH_4, GeH_4, SnH_4, and any other regular tetrahedral molecule?

INDEPENDENT STUDY

What are the bond angles in tetrahedral molecules such as CH_3Cl, CH_3Br, and BrO_3F, whose shapes are not regular tetrahedrons? Explain the differences.

What other methods do chemists use to determine bond angles?

What are other quantitative aspects of molecules that chemists measure and use? ●

Chapter 2 Test

1. What can you conclude about the vectors $\vec{u}$ and $\vec{v}$ if
   a. $\vec{u} \cdot \vec{v} = 0$
   b. $\vec{u} \cdot \vec{v} = |\vec{u}||\vec{v}|$
   c. $\vec{u} \times \vec{v} = \vec{0}$
   d. $|\vec{u} \times \vec{v}| = |\vec{u}||\vec{v}|$
   e. $(\vec{u} \times \vec{v}) \cdot \vec{u} = 0$
   f. $(\vec{u} \times \vec{v}) \times \vec{u} = \vec{0}$

2. Given $\vec{u} = 6\hat{i} + 3\hat{j} + 2\hat{k}$ and $\vec{v} = -3\hat{i} + 4\hat{j} + \hat{k}$, find
   a. $4\vec{u} - 3\vec{v}$
   b. $\vec{u} \cdot \vec{v}$
   c. $\vec{u} \times \vec{v}$
   d. a unit vector perpendicular to both $\vec{u}$ and $\vec{v}$

3. a. Draw x-, y-, and z-axes and make a sketch of
      i. the position vector $\overrightarrow{OP}$ of the point $P(3, -2, 5)$
      ii. the projection of $\overrightarrow{OP}$ onto the z-axis
      iii. the projection of $\overrightarrow{OP}$ onto the xy-plane
   b. Determine the magnitudes of the projections in **a**, parts **ii** and **iii.**

4. A parallelogram $ABCD$ has vertices $A(-1, 2, -1)$, $B(2, -1, 3)$, and $D(-3, 1, -3)$. Determine
   a. the coordinates of C
   b. the angle at A
   c. the area

5. A box is dragged 16 m across a level floor by a 75-N force at an angle of 35° to the floor. It is then dragged by the same force 8 m up a ramp inclined at an angle of 20° to the floor. Determine the total work done by the force.

6. A force of 50 N acts at the end of a wrench 18 cm long.

   a. In what direction should the force act to produce the maximum torque? (Draw a diagram.)

   b. What is the maximum torque? (State both magnitude and direction.)

   c. At what angle will the force produce half the maximum torque? Indicate this angle on your diagram.

7. Use the dot product to find an expression for the cosine of the acute angle between the diagonals of a rectangle with sides $\vec{a}$ and $\vec{b}$.

You have seen examples of geometric and algebraic vectors. A third common type of vector is the 0 - 1 string vector. Such vectors are composed of 0s and 1s in a row. A vector of length four might be 0010, or 1010, or 1111, and so on. Such vectors, because they correspond to current on (1) or current off (0), are of great value in computer communication.

Using strings of length 5 allows for the creation of 32 strings:
00000, 00001, 00011, ..., 11111.

Satisfy yourself that there are 32 length-5 strings.

Using 26 of these we can define the alphabet as follows:

A: 00001	G: 00111	M: 01101	S: 10011	Y: 11001
B: 00010	H: 01000	N: 01110	T: 10100	Z: 11010
C: 00011	I: 01001	O: 01111	U: 10101	
D: 00100	J: 01010	P: 10000	V: 10110	
E: 00101	K: 01011	Q: 10001	W: 10111	
F: 00110	L: 01100	R: 10010	X: 11000	

If you are familiar with binary numbers, you will note that this is a simple assignment of the number 1 in a five-digit display to represent A, the number 2 to represent B, and so on. The first advantage gained is that this allows the simple transmission of messages.

Using this system, the message *This is clever* can be transmitted as
10100010000100110011010011001100011011000010110110001011001 0.

Note that it is up to the receiver to create words from a string of letters and that, unless one of the unused strings is designated for the purpose, there is no punctuation.

The weakness of this system is that messages such as this are easily intercepted. They are not very secure if privacy is desired. This problem is, surprisingly, easily overcome by defining an arithmetic of addition (and subtraction) which can effectively *hide* the message. This provides the foundation of *cryptography*, the art of secret messages.

We define addition as follows:

a. $0 + 0 = 0$ $1 + 0 = 1$
$0 + 1 = 1$ $1 + 1 = 0$

b. There is no "carrying" from column to column.

The only surprise in the addition process is $1 + 1 = 0$. There are two reasons for this. The first is that adding five-digit strings will always give a five-digit result. The second is due to electronic properties. In a room with light switches at both ends of the room, the lights are off if both switches are off (0 position) OR if both switches are on (1 position). Hence, the addition works easily in electronic form.

Using this definition, we illustrate addition:

10010	01101
11011	01001
01001	00100

In the first example, 10010 (R) now looks as though it is 01001 (I), and a person intercepting the message will have a difficult time in determining the true message.

By adding a five-digit *key*, messages can be encrypted and interceptors cannot decode the transmitted message. For example, using the key 11101 for each letter, the word *MATH* becomes:

Key 01101000011010001000
Add 11101111011110111101
     10000111000100110101   (Send this)

An interceptor would translate this to P?IU and be confused. A person receiving the message and knowing the key merely reverses the process, as follows:

       10000111000100110101
Key   11101111011110111101   Note that subtraction is $\begin{bmatrix} 0-0=0, 1-1=0, \\ 1-0=1, 0-1=1 \end{bmatrix}$
       01101000011010001000   identical with addition.

The message is retrieved!

You can easily create messages in code. For interest, work with two friends and try the following:

1. Choose a key known to two but not the third.

2. Encrypt a message and give it to your friends.

3. The person knowing the key will be able to decrypt the message. It will be a real challenge for the remaining person to do so.

Discussion
You can increase the complexity of the deciphering by using vectors of length 6, 7, or 8. Discuss the effect of doing so.

Chapter 3

LINES IN A PLANE

When we solve geometric problems in two-dimensional space, Euclid's methods are usually sufficient for problems involving polygons and circles. For solving problems involving curves such as parabolas, ellipses, and hyperbolas, however, the analytic geometry of Descartes, using the language of algebra, is a superior tool. Both Euclidean and analytic methods are used for solving problems in three-dimensional space as well, but vector methods are more powerful than either the Euclidean or the analytic method. There are well-established formulas for finding the slope or direction of a line in two-dimensional space, but

how do you express direction in three-dimensional space? There are also formulas for lines in two-dimensional space, but are there corresponding formulas for lines in three-dimensional space? In this chapter, we will use vectors to develop these formulas and to solve problems involving points and lines in two and three dimensions.

CHAPTER EXPECTATIONS In this chapter, you will

- determine equations of lines in two- and three-dimensional space, **Section 3.1, 3.2, 3.3, 3.4**
- solve problems involving intersections of lines and planes, **Section 3.4**

Review of Prerequisite Skills

In this chapter and the next, vectors are used to investigate the geometry of straight lines and Euclidean planes in two and three dimensions. Lines are not vectors, but vectors are used to describe lines. Their similarities and differences are presented in the following table.

Lines	Vectors
Lines are bi-directional. A line defines a direction, but there is nothing to distinguish forward from backward.	Vectors are unidirectional. A vector defines a direction with a clear distinction between forward and backward.
A line is infinite in extent in both directions. A line segment has a finite length.	Vectors have a finite magnitude.
Lines and line segments have a definite location. The opposite sides of a parallelogram are two different line segments.	A vector has no fixed location. The opposite sides of a parallelogram are described by the same vector.
Two lines are the same when they have the same direction and same location. Such lines are said to be coincident.	Two vectors are the same when they have the same direction and the same magnitude. Such vectors are said to be equal.

The equation of a straight line in a plane in the form $y = mx + b$ is familiar from earlier mathematics courses. This equation is not suitable for describing the equation of a line in space. In this chapter, a new form of the equation of a line based on vectors is developed, one that can be extended from two to three dimensions. We will also develop the principal concepts needed to solve problems about the intersections of and distances between straight lines in both two and three dimensions.

Some forms of mathematics use creativity and imagination in a way that is similar to artistic creation. It is not uncommon to hear mathematicians refer to theorems as *elegant* or even *beautiful*. Sometimes mathematicians produce interesting, even beautiful, images.

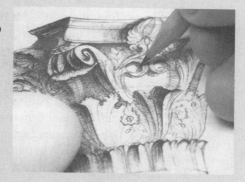

Investigate and Inquire

One way to create interesting images is through the use of parametric equations. These will be defined more precisely in Chapter 4, but one example of a set of parametric equations is $x = t - 2\sin(t)$, $y = 1 - \cos(t)$, $t \geq 0$. Here, each value of t gives a point (x, y). For example, if $t = \pi$ radians, then $(x, y) = (\pi, 2)$. As t increases, the point moves through the plane. The result is shown below.

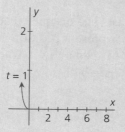

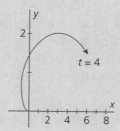

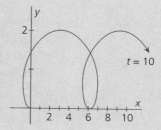

This figure is called a trochoid. Try drawing this on a graphing calculator. (*Note:* When working with parametric curves, we will evaluate trigonometric functions using radians.)

Many parametric equations can be interpreted as the position of a particle, at time t, as it moves through the plane.

DISCUSSION QUESTIONS

1. How can parametric equations be used to describe a curve in three dimensions? What about four or more dimensions?

2. When has mathematics required you to be creative, to use your imagination? Why does math sometimes seem unlike art?

3. How has mathematics been used in artistic practices? ●

Section 3.1 — Parametric and Vector Equations of a Line in a Plane

Imagine you are travelling at a constant speed along a perfectly straight highway that runs south and east from point A toward point B. As you travel, your position, P, changes from moment to moment, depending on how much time, t, has passed since leaving point A. The x- and y-coordinates of your position depend on t, but how? What are the equations which relate x and y to t?

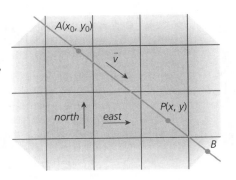

Your velocity $\vec{v}$ is a vector (v_x, v_y). In this vector, v_x is the eastward (x) component, which will be positive in this example. v_y is the northward (y) component, which will be negative in this example, since you are travelling to the south.

Consider first your motion toward the east. The distance that you have travelled east is the difference $x - x_0$ between your present position at point P and your starting position at point A. This distance is equal to $v_x t$, where v_x is the eastward component of your velocity, and t is the length of time you have been travelling: $x - x_0 = v_x t$.

Therefore $\qquad\qquad x = x_0 + v_x t$

In like manner $\qquad y = y_0 + v_y t$

This pair of equations gives your position $P(x, y)$ on the highway at any time t, after starting from $A(x_0, y_0)$.

The highway from A to B is a straight line. It is important to realize that the equations derived above represent a new and different way to describe this straight line. Unlike the familiar formula $y = mx + b$, which expresses y as a function of x, here each of the coordinates x and y is expressed separately in terms of a third variable, t.

In mathematics, when you describe a relation between two variables in an indirect manner using a third variable, the third variable is called a **parameter**. Equations that show how the two variables depend on that parameter are called **parametric equations**.

The **parametric equations** of a straight line in a plane have the form

$$x = x_0 + at$$
$$y = y_0 + bt$$

where (x, y) is the position vector of any point on the line,
(x_0, y_0) is the position vector of some particular point on the line,
(a, b) is a *direction vector* for the line,
and $t \in R$ is the parameter.

The parameter t, which represents the travel time above, is a real number that can take on any value. Just as each point in time corresponds to a position on the highway, each value of t corresponds to a particular point on the line, and each point on the line is characterized by a unique value of t.

EXAMPLE 1

Highway 33 from Regina to Stoughton, Saskatchewan, is an almost straight line. Suppose you travel on this highway with a constant velocity (expressed in component form, where east and north are positive) $\vec{v} = (85, -65)$ km/h. How far south of Regina are you when you are at a position 102 km east of Regina?

Solution

The parametric equations are $x = x_0 + 85t$, $y = y_0 - 65t$, with $(x_0, y_0) = (0, 0)$.

Using the x-component of the velocity, $102 = 0 + 85t$, then $t = \frac{6}{5}$. Therefore, it takes $\frac{6}{5}$ of an hour, or 72 minutes, for you to reach a point on the highway that is 102 km east of Regina.

Then $y = 0 + (-65)\left(\frac{6}{5}\right)$ or $y = -78$. Consequently, at this point in time, you are at a position on the highway that is 78 km south of Regina.

The velocity vector, which in Example 1 was parallel to the highway, is an example of a direction vector. In general, any vector $\vec{d} = (a, b)$ parallel to a line may be used as a direction vector for the line. By choosing the vector $(85, -65)$ in the example, we indicate that the units are in kilometres and hours. This could be, for example, a vector from one point to another on the line. The diagram below shows how the direction vector for a line is related to its slope.

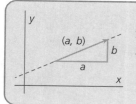

Any vector that is parallel to a line may be used as a **direction vector** for the line.
A line with **direction vector** (a, b) has **slope** $\frac{b}{a}$, provided $a \neq 0$.

EXAMPLE 2   State a direction vector for

a. the line that passes through the points $C(3, 4)$ and $D(7, 2)$

b. a line that has slope $-\dfrac{5}{3}$

c. a vertical line passing through the point $(-6, 5)$

Solution

a. The vector $\overrightarrow{CD}$ has components $(7 - 3, 2 - 4) = (4, -2)$. This vector or any scalar multiple of it such as $(2, -1)$ would be a suitable direction vector.

b. A line with a slope of $-\dfrac{5}{3}$ has a rise of -5 and a run of 3. The vector $(3, -5)$ is parallel to this line and would be a suitable direction vector.

c. A vector parallel to a vertical line has a horizontal component of zero. The simplest such vector is $(0, 1)$. So, even though the slope of a vertical line does not exist, a direction vector does. The point the line goes through is irrelevant.

EXAMPLE 3   A line passes through the point $(5, -2)$ with direction vector $(2, 6)$.

a. State the parametric equations of this line.

b. What point on the line corresponds to the parameter value $t = 3$?

c. Does the point $(1, -8)$ lie on this line?

d. Find the y-intercept and the slope of the line. Then, write the equation of the line in the form $y = mx + b$.

Solution

a. It is given that $(x_0, y_0) = (5, -2)$ and $(a, b) = (2, 6)$. The parametric equations of the line are

$$x = 5 + 2t$$
$$y = -2 + 6t, t \in R$$

b. When $t = 3$,
$$x = 5 + 2(3) = 11$$
$$y = -2 + 6(3) = 16$$

Therefore, the point $(11, 16)$ on the line corresponds to the parameter value $t = 3$.

c. To determine if $(1, -8)$ lies on the line, try to find its parameter value. Substitute $(1, -8)$ for (x, y) and solve for t.

$$1 = 5 + 2t \qquad -8 = -2 + 6t$$
$$t = -2 \qquad\qquad t = -1$$

There is no single parameter value that satisfies both equations. Therefore, the point $(1, -8)$ does not lie on the line.

d. To find the y-intercept, set $x = 0$ and find the values of t and then y.

$$0 = 5 + 2t \qquad \text{so} \quad t = -\frac{5}{2}$$
$$y = -2 + 6\left(-\frac{5}{2}\right) \quad \text{so} \quad y = -17$$

Since the direction vector is $(2, 6)$, the slope is $\frac{6}{2}$ or 3. Using the y-intercept -17, the equation of the line is $y = 3x - 17$.

Let us now look at the parametric equations of a line from a vector viewpoint. Recall that the ordered pair (x, y) can be reinterpreted as the position vector of the point $P(x, y)$. Therefore, the parametric equations of a line are equations about the x- and y-components of vectors. Consequently, we can combine the two parametric equations into one vector equation.

$$x = x_0 + at, \ y = y_0 + bt \ \text{ becomes } \ (x, y) = (x_0 + at, y_0 + bt)$$
$$\text{or } \ (x, y) = (x_0, y_0) + t(a, b)$$

The **vector equation** of a straight line in a plane has the form

$$\vec{r} = (x_0, y_0) + t(a, b)$$

where $\vec{r} = (x, y)$ is the position vector of any point on the line,
(x_0, y_0) is the position vector of some particular point on the line,
(a, b) is a direction vector for the line,
and $\quad t \in R$.

EXAMPLE 4

State a vector equation of the line passing through the points $P(4, 1)$ and $Q(7, -5)$.

Solution
The vector $\overrightarrow{PQ}$ from one point to the other on the line may be used as a direction vector, $\vec{d}$, for the line.

$$\vec{d} = \overrightarrow{OQ} - \overrightarrow{OP}$$
$$= (7, -5) - (4, 1)$$
$$= (3, -6)$$

Then, a vector equation of the line is $\vec{r} = (4, 1) + t(3, -6), t \in R$. You could also have used a shorter direction vector and the other point, so another vector equation of this line is $\vec{r} = (7, -5) + s(1, -2), s \in R$.

As Example 4 shows, the vector equation of a line has an unusual feature. Since any vector parallel to the line will do as a direction vector, and any point on the line can serve as the particular point required in the equation, two vector equations may look entirely different, yet still represent the same line. It is important, then, to determine whether or not two different vector equations in fact represent two different lines.

EXAMPLE 5

Are the lines represented by the following vector equations coincident? That is, do these equations represent the same straight line?

a. $\vec{r} = (3, 4) + s(2, -1)$ b. $\vec{r} = (-9, 10) + t(-6, 3)$

Solution
Check the direction vectors first.

a. $\vec{d_1} = (2, -1)$ b. $\vec{d_2} = (-6, 3)$

Since $\vec{d_2} = -3\vec{d_1}$, the direction vectors of the two lines are parallel.

To decide if the lines are coincident, we check to see whether a point on one of the lines satisfies the vector equation of the other. The point $(3, 4)$ is on the first line. If it is also on the second line, then $(3, 4) = (-9, 10) + t(-6, 3)$.

Then $3 = -9 - 6t$ and $4 = 10 + 3t$
       $t = -2$ $t = -2$

Since the same parameter value is obtained from each equation, the point $(3, 4)$ from the first line does lie on the second line, and the lines are coincident. (You may check in the same way that $(-9, 10)$ from the second line lies on the first line with $s = -6$.)

To summarize using vector language, the vector equation of a line is a formula that gives the position vector $\overrightarrow{OP}$ of any point on the line. The diagram shows that $\overrightarrow{OP}$ is the sum of the vectors $\overrightarrow{OP_0}$ to the line and $\overrightarrow{P_0P}$ along the line: $\overrightarrow{OP} = \overrightarrow{OP_0} + \overrightarrow{P_0P}$.

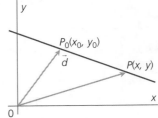

$\overrightarrow{OP_0}$ is the position vector (x_0, y_0) of a particular point on the line. $\overrightarrow{P_0P}$ is a scalar multiple of some direction vector (a, b) for the line. Consequently,

$$\overrightarrow{OP} = \overrightarrow{OP_0} + t\vec{d}$$
or $(x, y) = (x_0, y_0) + t(a, b)$
or $\vec{r} = \vec{r_0} + t\vec{d}$

Part A

1. What is a direction vector? What is a parameter? What role do these quantities play in the equation of a line?

2. State a direction vector for each of the following lines.

   a. a line parallel to $x = 9 - 3t$, $y = -4 + t$

   b. the line through $(6, 4)$ and $(-2, -6)$

   c. the line $y = 3x + 6$

   d. a line parallel to $\vec{r} = (1, 7) + t(4, 3)$

   e. a horizontal line

   f. a vertical line

3. State the coordinates of two points on each of the following lines.

   a. $x = 3 - 8t$, $y = 4t$ b. $\vec{r} = (4, 0) + t(0, 5)$

4. State a parametric equation and a vector equation for each of the following lines.

   a.
   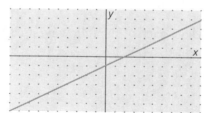

   b.
   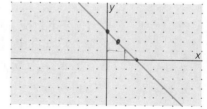

5. Graph the following lines.

   a. $x = -1 - 5t$
      $y = 6 + 2t$

   b. $\vec{r} = (-3, -4) + t(4, 3)$

6. For each of the following, find the parametric equations of the line that passes through the point P with direction vector $\vec{d}$. In each case, find two points on the line different from P.

   a. $P(1, 1)$, $\vec{d} = (4, -4)$ b. $P(5, 0)$, $\vec{d} = (1, 3)$

7. State parametric equations

   a. for the x-axis

   b. for a line parallel to but not coincident with the x-axis

Part B

8. For each of the following lines, find the vector equation that passes through the point P with direction vector $\vec{d}$.

   a. $P(-2, 7), \vec{d} = (3, -4)$ b. $P\left(2, \frac{3}{4}\right), \vec{d} = \left(\frac{2}{3}, 6\right)$

   c. $P(1, -1), \vec{d} = (-\sqrt{3}, 3)$ d. $P(0, 0), \vec{d} = (-2, 3)$

9. For each of the following lines, state a direction vector with integer components. If possible, name a point on the line with integer coordinates.

   a. $x = \frac{1}{3} + 2t, y = 3 - \frac{2}{3}t$

   b. $\vec{r} = \left(\frac{1}{3}, \frac{1}{2}\right) + t\left(\frac{1}{3}, \frac{1}{4}\right)$

   c. $\vec{r} = \left(\frac{1}{2}, 3\right) + t\left(-\frac{1}{2}, 5\right)$

10. For each of the following, determine which pairs of lines are parallel and which are perpendicular.

    a. $x = 1 - 3t, y = 7 + 4t$ and $x = 2 - 4s, y = -3s$

    b. $\vec{r} = (1, 7) + t(-3, 4)$ and $\vec{r} = (2, 0) + s(3, -4)$

    c. $\vec{r} = (1, 7) + t(-3, 4)$ and $\vec{r} = (2, 0) + s(4, -3)$

11. Find a vector equation of the line that passes through the point $(4, 5)$ and is perpendicular to the line $\vec{r} = (1, 8) + t(3, 7)$.

12. Find the points where each of the following lines intersects the x- and y-axes. Graph the line.

    a. $x = 6, y = 1 + 7t$

    b. $\vec{r} = (-5, 10) + t(1, 5)$

    c. $\vec{r} = (2, 3) + t(3, -1)$

13. Show that both lines $\vec{r} = (3, 9) + t(2, 5)$ and $\vec{r} = (-5, 6) + u(3, -1)$ contain the point $(1, 4)$. Find the acute angle of intersection of these lines to the nearest degree.

14. The angle α, $0° \leq \alpha \leq 180°$, that a line makes with the positive x-axis is called the **angle of inclination** of the line.

    a. Find the angle of inclination of each of the following lines.

       (i) $\vec{r} = (2, -6) + t(3, -4)$ (ii) $\vec{r} = (6, 1) + t(5, 1)$

    b. Prove that the tangent of the angle of inclination is equal to the slope of the line.

15. You are driving from point $A(24, 96)$ on a map grid toward point B with a velocity defined by $\vec{d}$ $(85, -65)$ km/h.

a. State the parametric equations of the highway line.

b. How long have you been travelling when you reach a point P 102 km east of where you started at point A?

c. What are the coordinates of your position P at that time?

16. a. By eliminating the parameter t from the parametric equations of a line, show that the equation of a line can be written in the form $\dfrac{x - x_0}{a} = \dfrac{y - y_0}{b}$ (provided neither a nor b is zero). This is known as the **symmetric equation** of a line.

b. Find a symmetric equation for each of the following lines.

(i) $x = 5 - 8t,\ y = -3 + 5t$ (ii) $\vec{r} = (0, -4) + t(4, 1)$

c. Find a symmetric equation for the line through the points $A(7, -2)$ and $B(-5, -4)$.

Part C

17. a. Show that $P(5, 8)$ and $Q(17, -22)$ are points on the line that passes through $A(7, 3)$ with direction vector $(2, -5)$.

b. Describe the line segment from $P(5, 8)$ to $Q(17, -22)$ using parametric equations with suitable restrictions on the parameter.

18. a. Suppose $\vec{p}$ and $\vec{q}$ are the position vectors of points P and Q in the plane. Show that the line that passes through P and Q has the vector equation $\vec{r} = (1 - t)\vec{p} + t\vec{q}$.

b. For what values of t does the point R with position vector $\vec{r}$ lie between points P and Q on the line?

c. When $t = 2$, draw a vector diagram that shows where point R with position vector $\vec{r}$ lies on the line relative to points P and Q.

d. For what values of t does the point R with position vector $\vec{r}$ lie closer to Q than P?

19. a. Find the vector equations of the two lines that bisect the angles between the lines
$$\vec{r_1} = (5, 2) + t(-3, 6)$$
$$\vec{r_2} = (5, 2) + u(11, 2)$$

b. Sketch all four lines.

c. Are the two lines that bisect the angles made by the intersecting lines always perpendicular? Explain.

Another way to form the equation of a line is to use a vector that is perpendicular to the line rather than one that is parallel to the line. Any vector that is perpendicular to a line is called a **normal vector** or simply a **normal** to the line.

EXAMPLE 1

Find a normal to the line

a. $y = -2x + 5$

b. $(x, y) = (2, -3) + t(2, 5), t \in R$

Solution

a. The slope of the given line is -2. The slope of a line perpendicular to the given line is $\frac{1}{2}$. A vector normal to the line is, therefore, $(2, 1)$.

b. The direction vector is $(2, 5)$. The dot product of $(2, 5)$ and any normal vector (n_1, n_2) must be zero.

$$(2, 5) \bullet (n_1, n_2) = 0$$
$$2n_1 + 5n_2 = 0$$

One of the many ways this equation can be satisfied is by choosing $n_1 = 5$ and $n_2 = -2$. Then, $(5, -2)$ is a normal to the line with direction vector $(2, 5)$.

The dot product of a normal vector and a direction vector is always zero because they are perpendicular. This is the key to the use of normal vectors in two dimensions.

EXAMPLE 2

Find the equation of the straight line with normal $(5, 2)$, which passes through the point $(-2, 1)$. Write the equation of the line in the form $Ax + By + C = 0$.

Solution

For a point $P(x, y)$ on the line, a direction vector is defined by

$$\overrightarrow{P_0P} = (x + 2, y - 1).$$

This vector is perpendicular to the normal.
The dot product of these vectors must be zero.

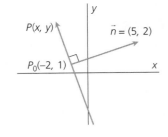

$$(5, 2) \bullet (x + 2, y - 1) = 0$$
$$5(x + 2) + 2(y - 1) = 0$$
$$5x + 10 + 2y - 2 = 0$$
$$5x + 2y + 8 = 0$$

This is the equation of the line through $(-2, 1)$ with normal $(5, 2)$.

In the equation found in Example 2, we can see that the components of the normal end up as the coefficients of the x- and y-terms. The following derivation demonstrates that this will always be the case.

The vector $\overrightarrow{P_0P}$ along a line from a fixed point $P_0(x_0, y_0)$ to any other point $P(x, y)$ must be perpendicular to the normal $\vec{n} = (A, B)$.

Then
$$\vec{n} \cdot \overrightarrow{P_0P} = 0$$
$$(A, B) \cdot (x - x_0, y - y_0) = 0$$
$$A(x - x_0) + B(y - y_0) = 0$$
$$Ax + By + (-Ax_0 - By_0) = 0$$
$$Ax + By + C = 0, \text{ where } C = -Ax_0 - By_0.$$

The **scalar** or **Cartesian equation** of a straight line in a plane has the form
$$Ax + By + C = 0$$
where the vector (A, B) is a normal to the line.

EXAMPLE 3

Find the scalar equation of the straight line with normal $(-6, 4)$ that passes through the point $(-3, -7)$.

Solution
Since $(-6, 4) = -2(3, -2)$ we can use $(3, -2)$ as a normal to the line. The equation must be of the form
$$3x - 2y + C = 0$$

Since the point $(-3, -7)$ lies on the line, its coordinates must satisfy the following equation.
$$3(-3) - 2(-7) + C = 0$$
$$C = -5$$

The equation of the line is $3x - 2y - 5 = 0$.

When the equation of a line is expressed in scalar form, it is a relatively straightforward task to find the distance from a point to the line. The shortest distance from the point Q to the line l is QN, measured along the normal through Q. This distance is shorter than the distance from Q to any other point P_0 on the line. (Why?)

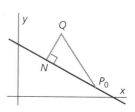

EXAMPLE 4

Find the distance from the point $Q(5, 8)$ to the line $7x + y - 23 = 0$.

Solution

In the diagram, the required distance is QN, where N is the point where the normal through Q meets the line. Then QN is the magnitude of the projection of $\overrightarrow{P_0Q}$ onto the normal to the line, where P_0 is any point on the line. Choosing P_0 to be $(3, 2)$ gives $\overrightarrow{P_0Q} = (2, 6)$. Also, $\vec{n} = (7, 1)$, so

$$QN = \left| \text{proj}(\overrightarrow{P_0Q} \text{ onto } \vec{n}) \right|$$

$$= \left| \frac{(2, 6) \cdot (7, 1)}{\sqrt{7^2 + 1^2}} \right|$$

$$= \left| \frac{14 + 6}{\sqrt{50}} \right|$$

$$= 2\sqrt{2}$$

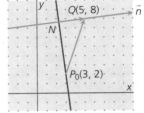

The distance from the point $Q(5, 8)$ to the line $7x + y - 23 = 0$ is $2\sqrt{2}$ units.

By working through the steps of the solution to Example 4 in general terms, we can find a simple formula for the distance from a point $Q(x_1, y_1)$ to a line with scalar equation $Ax + By + C = 0$. Letting $P_0(x_0, y_0)$ be a point on the line, the distance, d, is

$$d = \left| \text{proj}(\overrightarrow{P_0Q} \text{ onto } \vec{n}) \right|$$

$$= \left| \frac{\overrightarrow{P_0Q} \cdot \vec{n}}{|\vec{n}|} \right|$$

$$= \frac{\left| (x_1 - x_0, y_1 - y_0) \cdot (A, B) \right|}{\sqrt{A^2 + B^2}}$$

$$= \frac{\left| Ax_1 + By_1 - Ax_0 - By_0 \right|}{\sqrt{A^2 + B^2}}$$

Since $P_0(x_0, y_0)$ is on the line, it satisfies the equation of the line, so

$$Ax_0 + By_0 + C = 0$$

or $C = -Ax_0 - By_0$

Then the distance is $d = \dfrac{\left| Ax_1 + By_1 + C \right|}{\sqrt{A^2 + B^2}}$.

The **distance** from the point (x_1, y_1) to the line $Ax + By + C = 0$ is given by the formula

$$d = \frac{\left| Ax_1 + By_1 + C \right|}{\sqrt{A^2 + B^2}}.$$

Exercise 3.2

Part A

1. Explain why there is one and only one scalar equation of a given line, whereas there are many different parametric and vector equations for the line.

2. State a normal of the line that is

   a. perpendicular to $2x - 4y + 5 = 0$

   b. parallel to $2x - 4y + 5 = 0$

   c. perpendicular to $\vec{r} = (2, -5) + t(4, -2)$

   d. parallel to $\vec{r} = (2, 5) + t(4, -2)$

3. For each of the following, find the scalar equation of the line that passes through the point P_0 and has normal vector $\vec{n}$.

   a. $P_0(4, -2)$, $\vec{n} = (2, 7)$

   b. $P_0\left(\frac{1}{2}, 2\right)$, $\vec{n} = (-4, 0)$

   c. $P_0(3, 3)$, $\vec{n} = (1, 1)$

   d. $P_0\left(\frac{1}{3}, \frac{1}{3}\right)$, $\vec{n} = (-1, 1)$

4. For each of the following, find a normal vector, a direction vector, and a point on each line.

   a. $4x + 3y - 12 = 0$

   b. $3x - 6y = 14$

   c. $x = 5$

   d. $y = 3x - 10$

5. Prove that both $(-b, a)$ and $(b, -a)$ are perpendicular to (a, b) for all a and b.

6. Find the Cartesian equation of each of the following lines.

   a. $(x, y) = (4, -6) + t(8, 2)$

   b. $x = 3 + 18t, y = 4 + 9t$

   c. $\vec{r} = (2, 7) + t(2, 7)$

   d. $x = 2t, y = -2$

7. Find the scalar equation of the line that passes through $(2, -6)$ and

   a. is parallel to $2x - 3y + 8 = 0$

   b. is perpendicular to $3x - 2y + 12 = 0$

   c. has a direction vector $(2, -3)$

   d. has a normal vector $(3, -2)$

8. Find the scalar equation of the line through $(8, -2)$ that is parallel to the line $x = -4 - 5t, y = 11 + 3t$ by first finding the symmetric equation of this line, and then simplifying it.

Part B

9. Find vector, parametric, and symmetric equations of the following lines.

   a. $5x - 3y + 15 = 0$

   b. $-4x + 6y + 9 = 0$

10. Prove that the shortest distance from a point to a line is the distance measured along the perpendicular from the point to the line.

11. For each of the following, find the distance from $Q(3, -2)$ to each line.

    a. $3x - 2y - 6 = 0$

    b. $\frac{x-3}{2} = \frac{y-4}{7}$

    c. $\vec{r} = (-3, -7) + t\left(\frac{1}{5}, \frac{1}{6}\right)$

    d. $x = -5$

12. Find the distance from each of the following points to the line
    $6x + 3y - 10 = 0$.

    a. $(4, 7)$

    b. $(4, -8)$

    c. $(0, 5)$

    d. $\left(5, -\frac{20}{3}\right)$

Part C

13. a. Prove that two lines in a plane are parallel if and only if their normals are parallel.

    b. Prove that two lines in a plane are perpendicular if and only if their normals are perpendicular.

14. a. Show that the equation of a line that has an angle of inclination α can be expressed in the form $x \sin \alpha - y \cos \alpha + C = 0$. (See Exercise 3.1, Question 14.)

    b. Find the angle of inclination of $2x + 4y + 9 = 0$.

    c. Find the scalar equation of the line through the point $(6, -4)$ with an angle of inclination of $120°$.

15. Draw any line through point $A(2, 2)$. Through point $B(8, 10)$, draw a normal to the line through A, meeting it at the point $N(x, y)$.

    a. Show that N is a point on the circle defined by $\overrightarrow{AN} \cdot \overrightarrow{BN} = 0$.

    b. Describe the relationship between this circle and the points A and B.

16. $\vec{n}$ is a normal to a line and $\overrightarrow{OP}$ is the position vector of a point $P(x, y)$ on the line.

    a. Using diagrams, show that the line goes through the origin when $\vec{n} \cdot \overrightarrow{OP} = 0$.

    b. Prove that the line goes through the origin if and only if $\vec{n} \cdot \overrightarrow{OP} = 0$.

Section 3.3 — Equations of a Line in 3-Space

In generalizing the equations for a line from a two-dimensional plane to a three-dimensional space, we must introduce a z-coordinate for points and a z-component for vectors. The equations are otherwise very similar, except that there is no scalar equation of a line in space because a line in space does not have a unique normal.

> The **vector equation** of a straight line in space has the form
> $$\overrightarrow{OP} = \overrightarrow{OP_0} + t\vec{d}$$
> or $\quad \vec{r} = \vec{r_0} + t\vec{d}$
>
> or $\quad (x, y, z) = (x_0, y_0, z_0) + t(a, b, c)$
>
> where $\vec{r}$ is the position vector of any point on the line,
> $\qquad \vec{r_0}$ is the position vector of some particular point on the line,
> $\qquad \vec{d}$ is a direction vector for the line,
> and $\quad t \in R.$

The numbers a, b, and c, which are the components of the direction vector, are known as **direction numbers** of the line.

EXAMPLE 1

Determine a direction vector for

a. the line that passes through the points $P(6, -4, 1)$ and $Q(2, -8, -5)$
b. a line perpendicular to the xz-plane

Solution

a. $\overrightarrow{PQ} = \overrightarrow{OQ} - \overrightarrow{OP}$
$\qquad = (2, -8, -5) - (6, -4, 1)$
$\qquad = (-4, -4, -6)$

This vector or, better, $(-2, -2, -3)$ or, better still, $(2, 2, 3)$ could be used as a direction vector for this line.

b. A vector perpendicular to the xz-plane is parallel to the y-axis. A suitable direction vector is, therefore, $(0, 1, 0)$.

The position vector $\overrightarrow{OP}$ to a general point $P(x, y, z)$ on the line can be expressed as $\overrightarrow{OP} = \overrightarrow{OP_0} + \overrightarrow{P_0P}$. $\overrightarrow{OP_0}$ is the position vector of a particular point $P_0(x_0, y_0, z_0)$ on the line. $\overrightarrow{P_0P}$ is some scalar multiple of a direction vector.

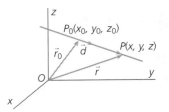

EXAMPLE 2

a. Find a vector equation of the line that passes through the point $P(1, 0, -1)$ and has direction numbers $(1, 2, 3)$.

b. Does the point $Q(-3, -8, -13)$ lie on this line?

Solution

a. A vector equation of the line is $\vec{r} = (1, 0, -1) + t(1, 2, 3)$.

b. The point $Q(-3, -8, -13)$ lies on the line only if there is a value of the parameter t such that

$$(-3, -8, -13) = (1, 0, -1) + t(1, 2, 3)$$

Then $\quad -3 = 1 + t \quad$ and $\quad -8 = 2t \quad$ and $\quad -13 = -1 + 3t$

or $\qquad t = -4 \qquad\qquad\qquad t = -4 \qquad\qquad\qquad t = -4$

This vector equation is satisfied by $t = -4$, so the point Q does lie on the line.

When each component of the vector equation is written out separately, the resulting equations are the parametric equations of a straight line in space.

The **parametric equations** of a straight line in space have the form

$$x = x_0 + at$$
$$y = y_0 + bt$$
$$z = z_0 + ct$$

where (x_0, y_0, z_0) are the coordinates of some particular point on the line, and a, b, and c are direction numbers for the line, and $\quad t \in R$.

Solving each of the parametric equations for the parameter t gives

$$t = \frac{x - x_0}{a}, \quad t = \frac{y - y_0}{b}, \quad \text{and } t = \frac{z - z_0}{c}$$

provided that none of a, b, or c is zero. These expressions give an alternate form for equations of a straight line in space.

> The **symmetric equations** of a straight line in space have the form
> $$\frac{x - x_0}{a} = \frac{y - y_0}{b} = \frac{z - z_0}{c}$$
> where (x_0, y_0, z_0) are the coordinates of some particular point on the line, and a, b, and c are direction numbers for the line with a, b, and $c \neq 0$.

EXAMPLE 3

Find vector, parametric, and symmetric equations of the line that passes through the points $A(2, -2, -8)$ and $B(5, -2, -14)$.

Solution
Since $\overrightarrow{AB} = (3, 0, -6)$, then $(1, 0, -2)$ is a direction vector for the line. Using A as the fixed point, a vector equation of the line is $\vec{r} = (2, -2, -8) + t(1, 0, -2)$.

Then the corresponding parametric equations are
$$x = 2 + t$$
$$y = -2$$
$$z = -8 - 2t$$

and the corresponding symmetric equations are
$$\frac{x - 2}{1} = \frac{z + 8}{-2}, y = -2$$

There is no symmetric expression for y because the corresponding direction number $b = 0$. In cases like this, when y does not change with t, you must still state its value. (If two direction numbers are 0, there is no symmetric equation.)

EXAMPLE 4

Write a vector equation for the line $-x = y + 2 = z$.

Solution
Rewriting the equations,
$$\frac{x - (0)}{-1} = \frac{y - (-2)}{1} = \frac{z - (0)}{1}$$

Then by inspection, a vector equation of the line is
$$\vec{r} = (0, -2, 0) + t(-1, 1, 1)$$

EXAMPLE 5

Do the equations $\frac{x - 5}{2} = \frac{y + 4}{-5} = \frac{z + 1}{3}$ and $\frac{x + 1}{-4} = \frac{y - 11}{10} = \frac{z + 4}{-6}$ represent the same line?

Solution

The direction vector of the second line $(-4, 10, -6)$ is -2 times the direction vector of the first line $(2, -5, 3)$, so the lines are parallel. They are coincident if the point $(-1, 11, -4)$ on the second line satisfies the equation of the first line.

$$\frac{(-1) - 5}{2} = -3, \frac{(11) + 4}{-5} = -3, \frac{(-4) + 1}{3} = -1$$

The fractions are not equal, therefore the lines are parallel and distinct.

EXAMPLE 6   Find vector, parametric, and symmetric equations of the *y*-axis, if possible.

Solution

The *y*-axis goes through the origin and has direction $\hat{j} = (0, 1, 0)$. A vector equation for the *y*-axis is $\vec{r} = (0, 1, 0)$ or simply $\vec{r} = t\hat{j}$. Parametric equations are $x = 0, y = t, z = 0$. It has no symmetric equation because two of the direction numbers are zero.

Exercise 3.3

Part A

1. Why does a line in space have a vector equation and a parametric equation, but no scalar equation?

2. Find a direction vector for a line
   a. parallel to $\vec{r} = (7, -9, 3) + t(-4, 2, -5)$
   b. through $(0, 6, 3)$ and $(7, 4, 6)$
   c. parallel to $-x = \frac{y - 3}{2} = \frac{z}{4}$

3. Give the coordinates of two points on each of the following lines.
   a. $\vec{r} = (1, 1, 2) + t(3, -1, -1)$
   b. $x = 4 - 2t, y = -2 + 5t, z = 5 + 4t$
   c. $\frac{x - 4}{3} = \frac{y + 5}{4} = \frac{z + 1}{-1}$

4. For each of the following, find vector, parametric, and, if possible, symmetric equations of the line that passes through P_0 and has direction vector $\vec{d}$.
   a. $P_0(2, 4, 6), \vec{d} = (-1, -3, 2)$
   b. $P_0(0, 0, -5), \vec{d} = (-1, 4, 1)$
   c. $P_0(1, 0, 0), \vec{d} = (0, 0, -1)$

5. List the points on the line $\vec{r} = (-2, 4, 3) + t(3, -1, 5)$ for even integer values of t from -6 to $+6$.

6. a. Which of the following points lies on the line $x = 2t$, $y = 3 + t$, $z = 1 + t$?

   $P(2, 4, 2)$ $Q(-2, 2, 1)$ $R(4, 5, 2)$ $S(6, 6, 2)$

   b. If the point $(a, b, -3)$ lies on the line, find the values of a and b.

Part B

7. Find parametric equations for the line that passes through the point $(0, -1, 1)$ and the midpoint of the line segment from $(2, 3, -2)$ to $(4, -1, 5)$.

8. Find symmetric equations for the line through the origin that is parallel to the line through the points $(4, 3, 1)$ and $(-2, -4, 3)$.

9. For each of the following pairs of equations, determine whether they represent the same line, parallel lines, or neither of these.

   a. $\vec{r} = (1, 0, 3) + s(3, -6, 3)$ and $\vec{r} = (2, -2, 5) + t(2, -4, 2)$

   b. $\vec{r} = (2, -1, 4) + s(3, 0, 6)$ and $\vec{r} = (-3, 0, 1) + t(2, 0, 2)$

   c. $\vec{r} = (1, -1, 1) + s(6, 2, 0)$ and $\vec{r} = (-5, -3, 1) + t(-9, -3, 0)$

10. Describe in words the lines having the following parametric equations. Sketch the lines.

    a. $x = t$, $y = 2$, $z = -1$

    b. $x = 0$, $y = 1 + t$, $z = 1 - t$

    c. $x = -5$, $y = 2 + t$, $z = 2 + t$

11. a. Describe the set of lines in space that have one direction number equal to zero.

    b. Describe the set of lines in space that have two direction numbers equal to zero.

Part C

12. Find the symmetric equations of the line that passes through the point $(-6, 4, 2)$ and is perpendicular to both of the lines
$$\frac{x}{-4} = \frac{y + 10}{-6} = \frac{z + 2}{3} \quad \text{and} \quad \frac{x - 5}{3} = \frac{y - 5}{2} = \frac{z + 5}{4}.$$

13. a. Show that the points $A(-9, -3, -16)$ and $B(6, 2, 14)$ lie on the line that passes through $(0, 0, 2)$ and has direction numbers $(3, 1, 6)$.

    b. Describe the line segment from A to B using parametric equations with suitable restrictions on the parameter.

14. Find an equation of the line through the point $(4, 5, 5)$ that meets the line $\frac{x - 11}{3} = \frac{y + 8}{-1} = \frac{z - 4}{1}$ at right angles.

15. a. Prove that the distance from a point Q in space to a line through a point P with direction vector $\vec{d}$ is equal to $\frac{|\vec{PQ} \times \vec{d}|}{|\vec{d}|}$.

    b. Find the distance from the point $Q(1, -2, -3)$ to the line $\vec{r} = (3, 1, 0) + t(1, 1, 2)$.

    c. Find the distance between the parallel lines $\vec{r} = (-2, 2, 1) + t(7, 3, -4)$ and $r = (2, -1, -2) + u(7, 3, -4)$.

Section 3.4 — The Intersection of Two Lines

What are the possible ways that two lines in a plane can intersect? They can be parallel (and distinct), intersecting at no points; they can cross, intersecting at a single point; or they can be coincident, thereby having an infinite number of common points.

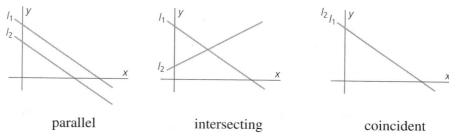

parallel   intersecting   coincident

When the equations of two lines are expressed in scalar form, you can find their point of intersection by the familiar method of elimination.

EXAMPLE 1

Find the intersection of the lines.
$$2x + 3y - 30 = 0$$
$$x - 2y + 13 = 0$$

Solution

Solving,
$$\begin{array}{r} 2x + 3y - 30 = 0 \\ -2x + 4y - 26 = 0 \\ \hline 7y - 56 = 0 \\ y = 8 \end{array}$$
Substitute in the second equation.

$$x - 2(8) + 13 = 0$$
$$x = 3$$

Therefore, the point of intersection is $(3, 8)$.

EXAMPLE 2

Find the intersection of the lines.
$$\vec{r} = (18, -2) + t(3, -2)$$
$$\vec{r} = (-5, 4) + s(2, 1)$$

Solution

First write the parametric equations of the lines.

line 1 $\quad x = 18 + 3t$ $\qquad\qquad$ **line 2** $\quad x = -5 + 2s$
$\qquad\qquad\ y = -2 - 2t$ $\qquad\qquad\qquad\qquad\qquad\ y = 4 + s$

Equating the expressions for x and y,

$\qquad 18 + 3t = -5 + 2s$ $\qquad$ or $\qquad 3t - 2s + 23 = 0$
$\qquad -2 - 2t = 4 + s$ $\qquad\qquad\qquad\qquad 2t + s + 6 = 0$

Solving, $s = 4$ and $t = -5$.

Substituting these into line 1 or into line 2, the coordinates of the intersection point are $(3, 8)$.

Like lines in a plane, lines in space can be parallel, intersecting at a point, or coincident. But there is also a new possibility: they can be **skew**. Skew lines are not parallel. Nevertheless, they do not intersect, because they lie in different planes. They just pass by each other like the vapour trails left by two aircraft flying at different altitudes.

EXAMPLE 3

Find the intersection of

line 1 $\quad \begin{cases} x = -1 + 3t \\ y = 1 + 4t \\ z = -2t \end{cases}$ $\quad$ and $\quad$ **line 2** $\quad \begin{cases} x = -1 + 2s \\ y = 3s \\ z = -7 + s \end{cases}$

Solution

Equating the expressions for x, y, and z gives

$\qquad -1 + 3t = -1 + 2s$ $\qquad$ or $\qquad 3t - 2s = 0$
$\qquad\ \ 1 + 4t = 3s$ $\qquad\qquad\qquad\qquad 4t - 3s + 1 = 0$
$\qquad\quad\ -2t = -7 + s$ $\qquad\qquad\qquad\ 2t + s - 7 = 0$

Solve for s and t using the second and third equations.

$\qquad\qquad$ **Equation 2** $\qquad\qquad 4t - 3s + 1 = 0$

$(-2) \times$ **Equation 3** $\qquad \dfrac{-4t - 2s + 14 = 0}{}$
$\qquad\qquad\qquad\qquad\qquad\qquad -5s + 15 = 0$
$\qquad\qquad\qquad\qquad\qquad\qquad\qquad\quad s = 3$

Substituting,

$\qquad\qquad\qquad\qquad\ 4t - 3(3) + 1 = 0$
$\qquad\qquad\qquad\qquad\qquad\qquad\quad t = 2$

Verify that $t = 2$ and $s = 3$ satisfy the first equation.

$$3t - 2s = 3(2) - 2(3)$$
$$= 6 - 6$$
$$= 0$$

Therefore, the two lines intersect at a unique point, which is the point determined by $t = 2$ on line 1, and $s = 3$ on line 2.
The point of intersection is $(5, 9, -4)$.

EXAMPLE 4

Find the intersection of

line 1	$\vec{r} = (2, 1, 0) + t(1, -1, 1)$
line 2	$\vec{r} = (3, 0, -1) + s(2, 3, -1)$

Solution

The direction vectors are not parallel, so the lines either intersect or are skew. The parametric equations are

line 1		line 2	
$x = 2 + t$		$x = 3 + 2s$	
$y = 1 - t$		$y = 3s$	
$z = t$		$z = -1 - s$	

Equating the expressions for x, y, and z gives

$$2 + t = 3 + 2s \qquad \text{or} \qquad t - 2s - 1 = 0$$
$$1 - t = 3s \qquad\qquad\qquad t + 3s - 1 = 0$$
$$t = -1 - s \qquad\qquad\qquad t + s + 1 = 0$$

Solving the first and second equations,

$$
\begin{array}{lr}
\textbf{Equation 1} & t - 2s - 1 = 0 \\
\textbf{(--1)} \times \textbf{Equation 2} & \underline{-t - 3s + 1 = 0} \\
& -5s = 0 \\
& s = 0, \text{ so } t = 1
\end{array}
$$

Finally, check to see if these values of t and s satisfy the third equation.

$$t + s + 1 = (1) + (0) + 1$$
$$= 2$$
$$\neq 0$$

The values of t and s do not satisfy the third equation. Therefore, the lines have no point of intersection. They are skew lines.

It is now time to place the subject of this section, intersections of lines, into a more general context. The scalar equation of a line is an example of a **linear equation.**

> **A linear equation** is an equation of the form
>
> $$a_1x_1 + a_2x_2 + a_3x_3 + \ldots = k$$
>
> where the x_i, ... are variables
> and the a_i, ... and k are constants.

The intersection problems considered in this section are elementary examples of **linear systems.** A linear system is a set of two or more linear equations and may involve thousands of equations. Problems requiring the solution of a linear system arise in disciplines such as engineering, economics, physics, and biology. In this section, the focus has been on the geometrical interpretation of a linear system and its solutions.

> **A system of linear equations** may have
> i) no solution
> ii) a unique solution
> iii) an infinite number of solutions

A linear system is said to be **consistent** if it has at least one solution. Otherwise, the system is **inconsistent.**

Solving a linear system when the number of equations is large is an extremely challenging problem, particularly if all coefficients are non-zero. Try to imagine the amount of work required to solve 10 equations with 10 variables. Fortunately, in real life many of the coefficients are zero.

You can get a reasonable picture of a real situation from the following examples. Suppose that a grocery store that stocks 50 different items has 50 customers. The first buys six different items worth $20, the second buys ten different items worth $37, the third buys seven different items worth $52, and so on. From this we can construct 50 equations in 50 variables, assuming that no two customers make identical purchases. From these equations we can determine the cost of each item.

Now picture the situation if there are 50 000 items in the store, or imagine the task of solving for 1 000 000 forces acting on the beams in a large building. It is true that many of the coefficients are zero. A system involving a large number of equations and having many coefficients equal to zero is referred to as a **sparse** system.

Solving such a system involves computer applications and clever algorithms. The study of linear systems is a highly developed area, and people skilled in analyzing such systems are greatly in demand.

Exercise 3.4

Part A

1. Line 1 intersects both the x-axis and the y-axis. Line 2 intersects only the z-axis. Neither contains the origin. Must the two lines be parallel or skew, or can they intersect?

2. Find the intersection point of each of the following pairs of lines. Graph the lines and identify the intersection point.

   a. $2x + 5y + 15 = 0$
   $3x - 4y + 11 = 0$

   b. $\vec{r} = (-3, -6) + s(1, 1)$
   $\vec{r} = (4, -8) + t(1, 2)$

3. Determine whether the following pairs of lines are coincident, parallel and distinct, or neither.

   a. $\frac{x-3}{10} = \frac{y-8}{-4}$
   $\frac{x-33}{-5} = \frac{y+4}{2}$

   b. $x = 6 - 18s, y = 12 + 3s$
   $x = 8 - 6t, y = 4 + 9t$

   c. $x = 8 + 12s, y = 4 - 4s, z = 3 - 6s$
   $x = 2 - 4t, y = 2 + t, z = 6 + 2t$

   d. $\frac{x+4}{3} = \frac{y-12}{4} = \frac{z-3}{6}$
   $\frac{x}{\frac{1}{2}} = \frac{y-10}{\frac{2}{3}} = z + 5$

Part B

4. Find the intersection of each pair of lines. If they do not meet, determine whether they are parallel and distinct or skew.

   a. $\vec{r} = (-2, 0, -3) + t(5, 1, 3)$
   $\vec{r} = (5, 8, -6) + u(-1, 2, -3)$

   b. $x = 1 + t, y = 1 + 2t, z = 1 - 3t$
   $x = 3 - 2u, y = 5 - 4u, z = -5 + 6u$

   c. $\vec{r} = (2, -1, 0) + t(1, 2, -3)$
   $\vec{r} = (-1, 1, 2) + u(-2, 1, 1)$

   d. $(x, y, z) = (1 + t, 2 + t, -t)$
   $(x, y, z) = (3 - 2u, 4 - 2u, -1 + 2u)$

   e. $\frac{x-3}{4} = y - 2 = z - 2$
   $\frac{x-2}{-3} = \frac{y+1}{2} = \frac{z-2}{-1}$

5. Consider the lines $\vec{r} = (1, -1, 1) + t(3, 2, 1)$ and
   $\vec{r} = (-2, -3, 0) + u(1, 2, 3)$.

   a. Find their point of intersection.

   b. Find a vector equation for the line perpendicular to both of the given lines that passes through their point of intersection.

6. Show that the lines $\vec{r} = (4, 7, -1) + t(4, 8, -4)$ and
   $\vec{r} = (1, 5, 4) + u(-1, 2, 3)$ intersect at right angles and find the point of intersection.

7. If they exist, find the x-, y-, and z-intercepts of the line $x = 24 + 7t$,
   $y = 4 + t, z = -20 - 5t$.

8. Find the point at which the normal through the point $(3, -4)$ to the line
   $10x + 4y - 101 = 0$ intersects the line.

Part C

9. What are the possible ways that three lines in a plane can intersect? Describe them all with diagrams.

10. What are the possible ways that three lines in space can intersect? Describe them all with diagrams.

11. Find the equation of the line through the point $(-5, -4, 2)$ that intersects the line at $\vec{r} = (7, -13, 8) + t(1, 2, -2)$ at 90°. Determine the point of intersection.

12. Find the points of intersection of the line $\vec{r} = (0, 5, 3) + t(1, -3, -2)$ with the sphere $x^2 + y^2 + z^2 = 6$. Is the segment of the line between the intersection points a diameter of the sphere?

13. Find a vector equation for the line through the origin that intersects both of the lines $\vec{r} = (2, -16, 19) + t(1, 1, -4)$ and $\vec{r} = (14, 19, -2) + u(-2, 1, 2)$.

14. a. Determine the point N at which the normal through the origin intersects the line $Ax + By + C = 0$ in the xy-plane.

    b. Find the magnitude of the position vector $\overrightarrow{ON}$ of point N.

15. The common perpendicular of two skew lines with direction vectors $\vec{d_1}$ and $\vec{d_2}$ is the line that intersects both the skew lines and has direction vector $\vec{n} = \vec{d_1} \times \vec{d_2}$. Find the points of intersection of the common perpendicular with each of the lines $(x, y, z) = (0, -1, 0) + s(1, 2, 1)$ and $(x, y, z) = (-2, 2, 0) + t(2, -1, 2)$.

16. The distance between the skew lines $\vec{r} = \overrightarrow{OP} + t\vec{d_1}$ and $\vec{r} = \overrightarrow{OQ} + s\vec{d_2}$ is $\left| \text{Proj}(\overrightarrow{PQ} \text{ onto } \vec{n}) \right|$ or $\dfrac{\left| \overrightarrow{PQ} \cdot \vec{n} \right|}{|\vec{n}|}$ where $\vec{n} = \vec{d_1} \times \vec{d_2}$.

Find the distance between the lines

a. $\vec{r} = (0, -2, 6) + t(2, 1, -1)$ and $\vec{r} = (0, -5, 0) + s(-1, 1, 2)$

b. $x = 6, y = -4 - t, z = t$ and $x = -2s, y = 5, z = 3 + s$

Key Concepts Review

This chapter has illustrated how the algebraic description of straight lines can be formulated in terms of vectors. The form of the vector equation of a line, $\vec{r} = \vec{r_0} + t\vec{d}$, is the same whether the line lies in a plane or in a three-dimensional space. This equation also describes a line in more abstract, higher dimensional spaces, where the vectors have more than three components.

To master this material, learn the various forms of the equation of a line.

the **vector equation**	$(x, y, z) = (x_0, y_0, z_0) + t(a, b, c)$ or $\vec{r} = \vec{r_0} + t\vec{d}$
the **parametric equations**	$x = x_0 + at, y = y_0 + bt, z = z_0 + ct$
the **symmetric equations**	$\dfrac{x - x_0}{a} = \dfrac{y - y_0}{b} = \dfrac{z - z_0}{c}$
the **scalar equation**	$Ax + By + C = 0$ (in two dimensions only)

Notice the position in each equation of the components (a, b, c) of the direction vector and the coordinates (x_0, y_0, z_0) of a point on the line. Work at converting from one form to another by inspection.

Try visualizing lines in three-dimensional space, perhaps using the lines along the corners of a room as coordinate axes. Practice sketching graphs of lines in two and three dimensions, remembering to move parallel to the axes when you plot coordinates of points or components of direction vectors.

Review Exercise

1. Consider any line in space that does not pass through the origin.
   a. Is it possible for this line to intersect just one coordinate axis? exactly two? all three? none at all?
   b. Is it possible for this line to intersect just one coordinate plane? exactly two? all three? none at all?

2. Find a vector equation of the line
   a. that passes through the points $(3, 9)$ and $(-4, 2)$
   b. that passes through the point $(-5, -3)$ and is parallel to the line $\vec{r} = (4, 0) + t(0, 5)$
   c. that is perpendicular to the line $2x - 5y - 6 = 0$ and passes through the point $(0, -3)$

3. Find parametric equations of the line
   a. that passes through $(-9, 8)$ with slope $-\frac{2}{3}$
   b. that passes through $(3, -2)$ and is perpendicular to the line $\vec{r} = (4, -1) + t(3, 2)$
   c. through the points $(4, 0)$ and $(0, -2)$

4. Find a vector equation of the line
   a. that passes through the points $(2, 0, -3)$ and $(-3, 2, -2)$
   b. that has an x-intercept of -7 and a z-intercept of 4
   c. that is parallel to $\dfrac{x - 5}{4} = \dfrac{y + 2}{-2} = \dfrac{z + 6}{5}$ and passes through the point $(0, 6, 0)$

5. Find parametric equations of the line
   a. that is parallel to the line $\dfrac{x + 1}{-3} = \dfrac{y + 2}{-2} = z + 3$ and passes through the origin
   b. that passes through the point $(6, -4, 5)$ and is parallel to the y-axis
   c. that has a z-intercept of -3 and direction vector $(1, -3, 6)$

6. Find the Cartesian equation of the line

   a. that passes through the point $(-1, -2)$ and is parallel to the line
      $3x - 4y + 5 = 0$

   b. that passes through the point $(-7, 3)$ and is perpendicular to the line
      $x = 2 + t, y = -3 + 2t$

   c. that passes through the origin and is perpendicular to the line
      $x + 4y + 1 = 0$

7. a. Find the parametric equations of the line l that passes through the point
      $A(6, 4, 0)$ and is parallel to the line passing through $B(-2, 0, 4)$ and
      $C(3, -2, 1)$.

   b. If $(-4, m, n)$ is a point on l, find m and n.

8. Determine if the following pairs of lines are parallel and distinct, coincident,
   perpendicular, or none of these.

   a. $\vec{r} = (2, 3) + t(-3, 1)$ and $\vec{r} = (-1, 4) + u(6, -2)$

   b. $x = 1 + 2t, y = -3 - t$ and $x = u, y = \frac{1}{3} + 2u$

   c. $\frac{x-1}{2} = \frac{y+4}{1}, z = 1$ and $x = 4t, y = 1 + 2t, z = 6$

   d. $(x, y, z) = (1, 7, 2) + t(-1, -1, 1)$ and $(x, y, z) = (-3, 0, 1) + u(2, -2, -2)$

9. At what points does the line $\frac{x+4}{2} = \frac{y-6}{-1} = \frac{z+2}{4}$ meet the coordinate
   planes?

10. In the xy-plane,

    a. find the Cartesian equation of the line $\vec{r} = (2, 3) + t(-1, 5)$

    b. find a vector equation of the line $5x - 2y + 10 = 0$

    c. find a vector equation of the line $y = \frac{3}{4}x + \frac{1}{2}$

11. Given the line $\vec{r} = (12, -8, -4) + t(-3, 4, 2)$,

    a. find the intersections with the coordinate planes, if any

    b. find the intercepts with the coordinate axes, if any

    c. graph the line in an x-, y-, z-coordinate system

12. Find the direction cosines and the direction angles (to the nearest degree) of
    the direction vectors of the following lines.

    a. $\frac{x-3}{5} = \frac{y+6}{2} = \frac{z-1}{-1}$

    b. $x = 1 + 8t, y = 2 - t, z = 4 - 4t$

    c. $\vec{r} = (-7, 0, 0) + t(4, 1, 0)$

13. Find the intersection, if any, of

    a. the line $\vec{r} = (0, 0, 2) + t(4, 3, 4)$ and the line
$\vec{r} = (-4, 1, 0) + u(-4, 1, -2)$

    b. the line $x = t, y = 1 + 2t, z = 3 - t$ and the line
$x = -3, y = -6 + 2u, z = 3 - 6u$

14. Find the shortest distance between

    a. the points $(2, 1, 3)$ and $(0, -4, 7)$

    b. the point $(3, 7)$ and the line $2x - 3y = 7$

    c. the point $(4, 0, 1)$ and the line $\vec{r} = (2, -2, 1) + t(1, 2, -1)$

    d. the point $(1, 3, 2)$ and the line $\dfrac{x-1}{-1} = \dfrac{y-3}{1} = \dfrac{z-7}{2}$

15. Find the coordinates of the foot of the perpendicular from $Q(3, 2, 4)$ to the line $\vec{r} = (-6, -7, -3) + t(5, 3, 4)$.

Rich Learning Link wrap-up
investigate and apply
CHAPTER 3: EQUATIONS OF LINES

Beauty is a cultural concept. What is beautiful to one person may not appeal to another. Nevertheless, when people consider the aesthetic qualities of an object, they usually consider some relationship between the complexity of the object and its orderliness. Repetition and symmetry are two ways in which an object may contain order.

Investigate and Apply

The exercises below require you to draw graphs. A graphing utility such as a graphing calculator will be helpful. Most graphing calculators have a mode setting that allows you to draw parametric curves. Remember to use radian mode.

1. Graph $x = 6 \cos t$, $y = 6 \sin t$, $0 \le t \le 2\pi$.

2. Find and verify parametric equations for an ellipse.

3. Graph $x = \frac{1}{2}t \cos t$, $y = \frac{1}{2}t \sin t$, $0 \le t \le 4\pi$.

4. Graph $x = \frac{4}{\cos t}$, $y = 3 \tan t$, $0 \le t \le 2\pi$.

5. Graph $x = 2t - 2 \sin t$, $y = 2 - 2 \cos t$, $t \ge 0$. The resulting shape is called a cycloid. It is a type of trochoid. It represents the path of a point on the edge of a circle as the circle rolls along the x-axis.

6. a) Graph an epicycloid: $x = 5 \cos t - 2 \cos\left(\frac{5t}{2}\right)$, $y = 5 \sin t - 2 \sin\left(\frac{5t}{2}\right)$, $0 \le t \le 4\pi$.

   b) Graph an epitrochoid: $x = 5 \cos t - 4 \cos\left(\frac{5t}{2}\right)$, $y = 5 \sin t - 4 \sin\left(\frac{5t}{2}\right)$, $0 \le t \le 4\pi$.

7. Graph a tricuspoid: $x = 6 \cos t + 3 \cos(2t)$, $y = 6 \sin t - 3 \sin(2t)$, $0 \le t \le 2\pi$.

8. Graph a Lissajous curve: $x = 8 \sin(3t + 1)$, $y = 8 \sin t$, $0 \le t \le 2\pi$.

9. What does $x = 6 \cos t$, $y = 6 \sin t$, $z = t$, $t \ge 0$ describe?

INDEPENDENT STUDY

Investigate: Find parametric equations for an Astroid, a hypocycloid, a Nephroid, a Plateau curve, and the Folium of Descartes.

Experiment: Create a parametric curve different from the ones you have seen here. Try to create one with features that make your curve unique.

Investigate: What are polar coordinates? What curves can be described using polar coordinates? ●

Chapter 3 Test

1. A line goes through the points $(9, 2)$ and $(3, 4)$. Determine
   a. its vector equation
   b. its parametric equations
   c. its symmetric equation
   d. its scalar equation

2. Find the scalar equation of the line which is perpendicular to the line $2x - 3y + 18 = 0$ and has the same y-intercept as the line $(x, y) = (0, 1) + t(-3, 4)$.

3. Find any two of the three intersections of the line $\frac{x - 2}{6} = \frac{y - 4}{3} = \frac{z + 2}{-3}$ with the coordinate planes, and graph the line.

4. Find the distance from the point $(1, -2, -3)$ to the line $x = y = z - 2$.

5. A line through the origin has direction angles $\beta = 120°$ and $\gamma = 45°$. Find a vector equation for the line.

6. Determine the point of intersection of the two lines $(x, y, z) = (-2, 0, -3) + t(5, 1, 3)$ and $\frac{x - 5}{-1} = \frac{y - 8}{2} = \frac{z + 6}{-3}$.

7. Let l_1: $x = -8 + t$, $y = -3 - 2t$, $z = 8 + 3t$ and l_2: $\frac{x - 1}{2} = \frac{y + 1}{1} = \frac{z}{3}$ be two lines in three-dimensional space.
   a. Show that l_1 and l_2 are skew lines (that is, neither parallel nor intersecting).
   b. State the coordinates of P_1, the point on l_1 determined by $t = -2$.
   c. Determine the coordinates of P_2, the point on l_2 such that $P_1 P_2$ is perpendicular to l_2.

The simple quadratic function $f(x) = rx(1 - x)$ where r is a specified constant can be used to demonstrate some of the most interesting ideas in modern mathematics. You can easily check that the graph of this function is symmetric about $x = \frac{1}{2}$ with a maximum value of $\frac{r}{4}$. We are interested in the function when $0 < x < 1$ and $0 < r < 4$ so that $0 < f(x) < 1$.

We can define a sequence by specifying x_0 and then each subsequent term by $x_n = f(x_{n-1})$, $n = 1, 2, ...$
If we start with $r = 2.0$ and $x_0 = 0.2$, we get
$x_1 = 2 \times 0.2 \times 0.8 = 0.32$, $x_2 = 0.4352$, $x_3 = 0.491602$, ... All terms are between 0 and 1.

It is easy to calculate the terms of this sequence on a spreadsheet. Note that the sequence can be written as $x_0, f(x_0), f(f(x_0)), f(f(f(x_0))), ...$

We can trace the development of the sequence on a plot of the function shown below. The line $y = x$ is also shown on the plot.

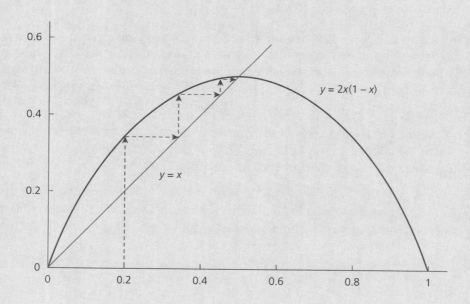

We start at the point $(0.2, 0)$. The next point is $(0.2, f(0.2))$. We then move horizontally to the line $y = x$ to get the point $(f(0.2), f(0.2))$. The next point is $(f(0.2), f(f(0.2)))$ and so on. The points on the curve have coordinates (x_n, x_{n+1}), $n = 0, 1, ...$.

The key question is to determine what happens as n gets large. In this case, we see that the terms of the sequence will approach 0.5. If we start with any value $0 < x_0 < 1$, then the sequence will converge to the same value — this is easy to see from the graph and to check with a spreadsheet calculation.

This does not seem very interesting. However, let's see what happens if we change the value of the multiplier to less and carry out the same calculations with $x_0 = 0.2$. The first few terms of the sequence are

n	0	1	2	3	4	5	6
x_n	0.2	0.512	0.800	0.513	0.799	0.513	0.799

If you construct the corresponding plot, you will see that there are now two points of convergence at 0.513 and 0.799. When n is large, the sequence oscillates between these two values. Most starting values produce the same limiting behaviour, but some, such as $x_0 = \frac{5}{16}$, produce a single point of convergence. Can you figure out why?

If we further increase r to 3.5, we find that there are four points of convergence for most starting points. In fact by slowly increasing r, we can get 8, 16, 32, ... points of convergence. The big surprise occurs about $r = 3.57$. Suddenly, there is no apparent pattern in the sequence for many starting points and there are no points of convergence. Different starting values lead to different sequences. The sequence is called *chaotic*. Try generating this sequence on a spreadsheet with $x_0 = 0.2$.

Even stranger, if we look at larger values of r, there are some values for which the sequence is chaotic and some for which there are regular oscillations. Write a spreadsheet program to try some values of x_0 and r. Can you produce the plot of the sequence as described above?

In the chaotic case, a very small change in the value of r can lead to a complete change of behaviour of the sequence. For mathematicians used to continuous behaviour, this abrupt change is fascinating. The study of this sequence and its generalizations is called *chaos theory*, a very active branch of modern mathematics.

Chapter 4
EQUATIONS OF PLANES

The concepts of point and line are as fundamental to geometry in three-dimensional space as they are in two-dimensional space. In three-dimensional space, however, we have another fundamental issue to consider, that of the plane. Is there such a thing as the equation or equations of a plane? Does a plane have a direction in space? In this chapter, we will look at the relationships between a point and a plane, a line and a plane, two planes, and even three planes.

CHAPTER EXPECTATIONS In this chapter, you will

- determine the vector, parametric, and scalar equations of planes, **Section 4.1, 4.2**
- determine the intersection of a line and a plane in three-dimensional space, **Section 4.3**
- determine the intersection of two or three planes, **Section 4.4**
- solve systems of linear equations involving up to three unknowns using row reduction of matrices, with and without the aid of technology, **Section 4.4**
- interpret row reduction of matrices as the creation of a new linear system equivalent to the original, **Section 4.4**
- interpret linear equations in two and three unknowns, **Section 4.5**

Review of Prerequisite Skills

Two points or one vector (a direction vector) and one point determine a line, a one-dimensional object. A third point not on that line opens the door to a second dimension. Thus, three non-collinear points or two non-collinear vectors and a point determine a plane, a two-dimensional object. Similarly, four non-coplanar points or three non-coplanar vectors determine a three-dimensional space. These concepts can be generalized to higher dimensional spaces, which despite their abstract nature have a surprising number of applications in the physical sciences, engineering, and economics.

The equation of a two-dimensional plane in a three-dimensional space has several forms. These are developed in the first part of this chapter in much the same way as those of a straight line.

Recall in particular

the **vector equation** $\qquad\qquad \vec{r} = \vec{r}_0 + t\vec{d}$

the **parametric equations** $\qquad x = x_0 + at$
$$y = y_0 + bt$$
$$z = z_0 + ct$$

the **scalar equation of a line** $\quad Ax + By + C = 0$
in **two-dimensional space**

Equations of lines and planes are essential parts of computer systems used by engineers and architects for computer-assisted design.

The remainder of this chapter is concerned with how lines can intersect with planes and planes can intersect with other planes. Intersection problems are geometrical models of linear systems. Therefore, this chapter includes an introduction to systematic methods for solving linear systems using matrices.

Astronomers have always sought methods for determining and predicting the positions of objects in the sky. One reason for doing this has been to test and improve upon our models of the solar system. In this way, astronomers have already learned, among other things, that the earth revolves around the sun once every 365.25 solar days in an elliptical orbit at a distance varying between 147.1 and 152.1 million kilometres. The earth rotates on its axis once every 23 hours, 56 minutes, and 4 seconds. This is known as a sidereal day. The axis of rotation is tilted 23.45° from perpendicular to the plane of the earth's orbit. We shall investigate, here and in the wrap-up at the end of the chapter, how to determine the angle of elevation of the sun at any given time of any given day at any given place on the surface of the earth.

Investigate and Inquire

The angle of elevation of the sun is the angle between the vector from the earth to the sun and the plane tangent to the surface of the earth. Planes will be studied in this chapter. Here we shall set out some groundwork for our calculations.

We will make the following assumptions to simplify our calculations: the earth is a perfect sphere that orbits the sun every 365 days in a perfect circle whose radius is 150 million kilometres. We shall let d be the number of solar days past December 21, the date of the winter solstice in the northern hemisphere. We will assume that at noon on December 21, the north pole is pointed away from the sun as much as possible. We let h be the number of hours (positive or negative) from noon. Noon here means the time when the sun is highest, regardless of the standardized time-zone time. It is the time halfway between sunrise and sunset. Let θ be the latitude of the observer.

If we place the sun at the origin of a three-dimensional Cartesian coordinate system, we can parameterize the earth's orbit in the xy-plane as

$x = -150 \sin\left(\frac{360d}{365}\right)$, $y = 150 \sin\left(\frac{360d}{365}\right)$. (See the Rich Learning Link on parametric curves in Chapter 3.) The vector $\vec{s}$, from the earth to the sun, will be $\vec{s} = (-x, -y, 0) = \left(150 \sin\left(\frac{360d}{365}\right), -150 \cos\left(\frac{360d}{365}\right), 0\right)$. Why is it $(-x, -y, 0)$ and not $(x, y, 0)$?

DISCUSSION QUESTIONS

1. What is the angle of elevation of the sun at sunrise and sunset? How might we interpret a negative angle of elevation?

2. Why is there a difference between the length of the solar day (the 24 hours between successive noons) and the sidereal day? ●

The vector equation of a plane gives the position vector $\overrightarrow{OP}$ of any point $P(x, y, z)$ in the plane. It is constructed in the same way as the vector equation of a line. First, write the position vector $\overrightarrow{OP}$ as the sum of two vectors: $\overrightarrow{OP_0}$, the vector from the origin to some particular point $P_0(x_0, y_0, z_0)$ in the plane, and $\overrightarrow{P_0P}$, the vector from the particular point P_0 to the general point P.

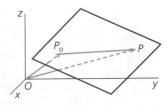

$$\overrightarrow{OP} = \overrightarrow{OP_0} + \overrightarrow{P_0P}$$

Now, choose two non-collinear vectors in the plane as basis vectors for the plane. Call them $\vec{a}$ and $\vec{b}$. These two vectors are known as direction vectors for the plane. Express the point-to-point vector $\overrightarrow{P_0P}$ as a linear combination of $\vec{a}$ and $\vec{b}$. We write

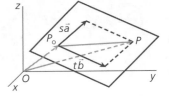

$$\overrightarrow{P_0P} = s\vec{a} + t\vec{b}$$

Therefore, $\overrightarrow{OP} = \overrightarrow{OP_0} + s\vec{a} + t\vec{b}$

or, letting $\vec{r}$ and $\vec{r_0}$ stand for the position vectors $\overrightarrow{OP}$ and $\overrightarrow{OP_0}$, respectively,

$$\vec{r} = \vec{r_0} + s\vec{a} + t\vec{b}$$

The **vector equation of a plane** has the form

$$\vec{r} = \vec{r_0} + s\vec{a} + t\vec{b}$$

where $\vec{a}$ and $\vec{b}$ are direction vectors for the plane,
          $\vec{r_0}$ is the position vector of a particular point in the plane,

and $s, t \in R.$

The coefficients s and t in the vector equation of a plane are parameters. There are two parameters because a plane is two-dimensional. The parametric equations of the plane are equations for the components of $\vec{r}$.

The **parametric equations of a plane** have the form

$$x = x_0 + sa_1 + tb_1$$
$$y = y_0 + sa_2 + tb_2$$
$$z = z_0 + sa_3 + tb_3$$

where (a_1, a_2, a_3) and (b_1, b_2, b_3) are components of
the direction vectors $\vec{a}$ and $\vec{b}$ for the plane,
(x_0, y_0, z_0) are components of the position
vector of a specific point in the plane,

and $s, t \in R.$

In reality, a plane is a flat surface that extends infinitely in all directions. In the diagrams on page 122, we have depicted a plane using a parallelogram. This gives a three-dimensional perspective to the diagrams and suggests that the plane may be oriented at some angle to the coordinate axes. Although not true graphs, such diagrams are adequate for analyzing most problems about lines and planes in three dimensions.

EXAMPLE 1

Find vector and parametric equations of the plane that contains the three points $A(1, 0, -3)$, $B(2, -3, 1)$, and $C(3, 5, -3)$.

Solution

The point-to-point vectors $\overrightarrow{AB}$ and $\overrightarrow{AC}$ both lie in the plane. They are

$$\overrightarrow{AB} = (1, -3, 4)$$
$$\overrightarrow{AC} = (2, 5, 0)$$

Since these vectors are non-collinear, they can serve as direction vectors for the plane. Taking point A as the given point, $\vec{r}_0 = \overrightarrow{OA} = (1, 0, -3)$. Therefore, a vector equation of the plane is

$$\vec{r} = (1, 0, -3) + s(1, -3, 4) + t(2, 5, 0)$$

The parametric equations can be written down by inspection.

$$x = 1 + s + 2t$$
$$y = -3s + 5t$$
$$z = -3 + 4s$$

It should be clear that the vector and parametric equations of a plane are not unique. In Example 1, if $\overrightarrow{BA}$ and $\overrightarrow{BC}$ had been chosen as direction vectors and point B as the given point, then the vector equation would have been

$$r = (2, -3, 1) + s(-1, 3, -4) + t(1, 8, -4)$$

When two equations look entirely different, how do you decide if they represent the same plane? This question will be addressed in the next section.

EXAMPLE 2

Does the point $(4, 5, -3)$ lie in the plane $\vec{r} = (4, 1, 6) + p(3, -2, 1) + q(-6, 6, -1)$?

Solution

The parametric equations are

$$x = 4 + 3p - 6q$$
$$y = 1 - 2p + 6q$$
$$z = 6 + p - q$$

If the point lies in the plane, the coordinates of the point $(4, 5, -3)$ must satisfy these equations. Substitution gives

$$
\begin{array}{ccc}
4 = 4 + 3p - 6q & \quad\text{or}\quad & 3p - 6q = 0 \\
5 = 1 - 2p + 6q & & -2p + 6q = 4 \\
-3 = 6 + p - q & & p - q = -9
\end{array}
$$

Solving the first two equations gives $p = 4$, $q = 2$. But these values of p and q do not satisfy the third equation. Therefore, the point does not lie in the plane. You can also see that these values of p and q produce $z = 8$ for the z-coordinate of the point, not $z = -3$ as they should.

EXAMPLE 3

Find the vector equation of the plane that contains the two parallel lines

$$l_1: \vec{r} = (2, 4, 1) + t(3, -1, 1)$$
$$l_2: \vec{r} = (1, 4, 4) + t(-6, 2, -2)$$

Solution

We take $(2, 4, 1)$ from l_1 as the position vector $\vec{r}_0$ of a given point on the plane and $(3, -1, 1)$ as $\vec{a}$, one of the direction vectors.

For the second direction vector, use the point-to-point vector between the given points on the two lines, $(1, 4, 4) - (2, 4, 1) = (-1, 0, 3)$. A vector equation of the plane is thus

$$\vec{r} = (2, 4, 1) + t(3, -1, -1) + s(-1, 0, 3).$$

Part **A**

1. Why does the vector equation of a plane have two parameters while the vector equation of a line has only one?

2. a. State two direction vectors for the xz-coordinate plane.

   b. What do all direction vectors for the xz-coordinate plane have in common?

3. State two direction vectors for each of the following planes.

   a. $\vec{r} = (9, 5, 2) + s(-3, 5, 2) + t(-6, 1, 2)$

   b. a plane parallel to the plane $x = 3 + 5s + t$
   $$y = -2 - 5s + 6t$$
   $$z = -2 + 3s - 2t$$

   c. the plane containing the intersecting lines $\vec{r} = (6, 5, -2) + s(4, -2, 1)$ and $\vec{r} = (-10, -3, 1) + t(-1, 5, 2)$

4. State two points that lie on each of the following planes.

   a. $\vec{r} = (9, 4, -3) + t(-2, 2, 1) + p(0, -2, 6)$

   b. $\vec{r} = (0, 1, 0) + t(1, 0, -2) + p(0, 0, 4)$

   c. $x = 3 + 5s + t$
   $$y = -2 - 5s + 6t$$
   $$z = -2 + 3s - 2t$$

   d. the xz-plane

5. Write parametric equations for each of these planes.

   a. $\vec{r} = (-4, -6, 3) + s(5, 2, 3) + t(-4, -6, 3)$

   b. $\vec{r} = (0, 0, 1) + s(0, 2, 0) + t(3, 0, 0)$

   c. the xz-plane

6. Write a vector equation for each of these planes.

   a. $x = -4 + s + 3t$ b. $x = 7s$ c. the xz-plane
   $$y = -1 + 3s - 4t$$ $$y = 4$$
   $$z = 3 + 4s - t$$ $$z = -2t$$

7. Determine a vector equation of each of the following planes.

    a. the plane through the point $(-4, 5, 1)$ parallel to the vectors $(-3, -5, 3)$ and $(2, -1, -5)$

    b. the plane containing the two intersecting lines $\vec{r} = (4, 7, 3) + t(1, 4, 3)$ and $\vec{r} = (-1, -4, 6) + s(-1, -1, 3)$

    c. the plane containing the line $\vec{r} = (-3, 4, 6) + t(-5, -2, 3)$ and the point $(8, 3, 5)$

    d. the plane containing the two parallel lines $\vec{r} = (0, 1, 3) + t(-6, -3, 6)$ and $\vec{r} = (-4, 5, -4) + s(4, 2, -4)$

    e. the plane containing the three points $(2, 6, -5)$, $(-3, 1, -4)$, and $(6, -2, 2)$

8. Determine parametric equations of each of the following planes.

    a. the plane through the point $(7, -5, 2)$ parallel to the vectors $(4, -1, 1)$ and $(-3, 4, 4)$

    b. the plane containing the two intersecting lines $\vec{r} = (5, 4, 2) + t(4, -2, 1)$ and $\vec{r} = (7, 4, -7) + s(-3, 1, 4)$

    c. the plane containing the line $\vec{r} = (1, 3, -1) + t(2, 2, -5)$ and the point $(8, 3, 5)$

    d. the plane containing the two parallel lines $\vec{r} = (3, 2, 2) + t(-9, 6, -6)$ and $\vec{r} = (1, 6, -6) + s(6, -4, 4)$

    e. the plane containing the three points $(2, 6, -5)$, $(-3, 1, -4)$, and $(6, -2, 2)$

9. Determine the vector equation of each of the following planes.

    a. the plane parallel to the yz-plane containing the point $(6, 4, 2)$

    b. the plane containing the origin and the points $(3, 3, 3)$ and $(8, -1, -1)$

    c. the plane containing the x-axis and the point $(-1, -4, -7)$

10. a. Explain why the three points $(2, 3, -1)$, $(8, 5, -5)$, and $(-1, 2, 1)$ *do not* determine a plane.

    b. Explain why the line $\vec{r} = (4, 9, -3) + t(1, -4, 2)$ and the point $(8, -7, 5)$ *do not* determine a plane.

11. Find vector and parametric equations of the plane that contains the line $x = 7 - t, y = -2t, z = -7 + t$ and that does not intersect the z-axis.

12. Demonstrate that a plane with a vector equation of the form $\vec{r} = (a, b, c) + s(d, e, f) + t(a, b, c)$ passes through the origin.

Part C

13. a. The vectors $\vec{a}, \vec{b},$ and $\vec{c}$ are the position vectors of three points A, B, and C. Show that $\vec{r} = p\vec{a} + s\vec{b} + t\vec{c}$, where $p + s + t = 1$ is an equation of the plane containing these three points.

    b. What region of the plane is determined by the equation, when the parameters s and t are restricted to the values $0 \le s \le 1$, and $0 \le t \le 1$? (*Hint:* Replace p with $(1 - s - t)$.)

14. a. The equation $\vec{r} = \vec{r}_0 + t\vec{d}$ is a vector equation of a line and $\vec{q}$ is the position vector of a point Q not on the line. Show that $\vec{r} = k\vec{r}_0 + l\vec{q} + t\vec{d}$, where $k + l = 1$ is an equation of the plane containing the line and the point.

    b. What region of the plane is determined by the equation, when the parameter k is restricted to $0 \le k \le 1$? (*Hint:* Replace l by $(1 - k)$.)

Any vector that is perpendicular to a plane is a **normal vector** or simply a **normal** to the plane. You can find the normal to a plane by finding the cross product of the two direction vectors of the plane. Since every vector in the plane can be represented as a linear combination of the direction vectors, the normal is perpendicular to every vector in the plane.

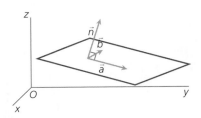

EXAMPLE 1

a. Find a normal to the plane with vector equation
$$\vec{r} = (3, 0, 2) + s(2, 0, -1) + t(6, 2, 0).$$

b. Show that the normal is perpendicular to every vector in the plane.

Solution

a. The two direction vectors of the plane are $(2, 0, -1)$ and $(6, 2, 0)$.
   The cross product of the direction vectors is $(2, 0, -1) \times (6, 2, 0) = (2, -6, 4)$.
   Thus, a normal to the plane is $(2, -6, 4)$ or $(1, -3, 2)$.

b. Any vector in the plane can be written as a linear combination of the two direction vectors, say $\vec{v} = p(2, 0, -1) + q(6, 2, 0)$. To show that the normal is perpendicular to $\vec{v}$, find the dot product.

$$
\begin{aligned}
\vec{v} \cdot \vec{n} &= [p(2, 0, -1) + q(6, 2, 0)] \cdot (1, -3, 2) \\
&= p(2, 0, -1) \cdot (1, -3, 2) + q(6, 2, 0) \cdot (1, -3, 2) \\
&= p(0) + q(0) \\
&= 0
\end{aligned}
$$

Since the dot product is zero, the two vectors must be perpendicular. This result is independent of the values of p and q.

You can use the fact that the normal to a plane is perpendicular to every vector in the plane to derive the scalar equation of a plane. Let $P(x, y, z)$ be any point in a plane with normal (A, B, C), and let $P_0(x_0, y_0, z_0)$ be some particular point in the plane. The vector $\overrightarrow{P_0P}$ must lie in the plane because its endpoints do. Therefore, it must be perpendicular to the normal (A, B, C), and their dot product must be zero.

$$
\begin{aligned}
(A, B, C) \cdot \overrightarrow{P_0P} &= 0 \\
(A, B, C) \cdot (x - x_0, y - y_0, z - z_0) &= 0 \\
A(x - x_0) + B(y - y_0) + C(z - z_0) &= 0 \\
Ax + By + Cz + (-Ax_0 - By_0 - Cz_0) &= 0
\end{aligned}
$$

The quantity in brackets is a constant because the components of the normal and the coordinates of the given point have particular numerical values.

Letting $D = (-Ax_0 - By_0 - Cz_0)$ the result is

$$Ax + By + Cz + D = 0.$$

The **scalar** or **Cartesian equation of a plane in space** is
$$Ax + By + Cz + D = 0$$
where (A, B, C) is a vector normal to the plane.

Unlike the vector equation, the scalar equation of a plane is unique. For instance, the equations $x + 2y + 3z + 4 = 0$ and $2x + 4y + 6z + 8 = 0$ represent the same plane, since one equation is a multiple of the other.

EXAMPLE 2

a. Find the scalar equation of the plane with vector equation
$$\vec{r} = (3, 0, 2) + p(2, 0, -1) + q(6, 2, 0).$$

b. Show that $\vec{r} = (-1, -2, 1) + s(5, 3, 2) + t(2, 4, 5)$ is another vector equation of the same plane.

Solution

a. In Example 1, a normal to this plane was found to be $(1, -3, 2)$. Therefore,

$$(A, B, C) = (1, -3, 2)$$
and $$x - 3y + 2z + D = 0$$

The vector $(3, 0, 2)$ is given as the position vector of a point on this plane. Then

$$(3) - 3(0) + 2(2) + D = 0$$
$$D = -7$$

Therefore, the scalar equation is $x - 3y + 2z - 7 = 0$.

b. For $\vec{r} = (-1, -2, 1) + s(5, 3, 2) + t(2, 4, 5)$, the normal is
$(5, 3, 2) \times (2, 4, 5) = (7, -21, 14)$.
Therefore, $(7, -21, 14)$ or $(1, -3, 2)$ is a normal to the plane.
The scalar equation of the plane is

$$x - 3y + 2z + D = 0$$

Now, substitute the point $(-1, -2, 1)$ into this equation to find D.

$$(-1) - 3(-2) + 2(1) + D = 0$$
$$D = -7$$

The scalar equation of this plane is $x - 3y + 2z - 7 = 0$, so the two vector equations represent the same plane, or the planes represented by the two vector equations are coincident.

The distance from a point to a plane in three dimensions is calculated in much the same way as the distance from a point to a line in two dimensions. It is measured along the normal to the plane. If Q is some point not in the plane and P_0 is any point in the plane, then the distance $|QN|$ from Q to the plane is the projection of $\overrightarrow{P_0Q}$ onto the normal $\vec{n}$.

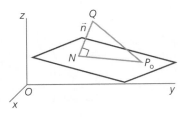

EXAMPLE 3

Find the distance from the point $Q(1, 3, -2)$ to the plane $4x - y - z + 6 = 0$.

Solution

The distance is the projection of $\overrightarrow{P_0Q}$ onto the normal $(4, -1, -1)$. For P_0, choose any point in the plane, say $(0, 0, 6)$. Then $\overrightarrow{P_0Q} = (1, 3, -8)$. The distance is then

$$d = |\text{Proj}(\overrightarrow{P_0Q} \text{ onto } \vec{n})|$$

$$= \frac{|\overrightarrow{P_0Q} \cdot \vec{n}|}{|\vec{n}|}$$

$$= \frac{|(1, 3, -8) \cdot (4, -1, -1)|}{\sqrt{(4)^2 + (-1)^2 + (-1)^2}}$$

$$= \frac{9}{\sqrt{18}}$$

$$= \frac{3}{\sqrt{2}}$$

$$= \frac{3\sqrt{2}}{2}$$

A general formula can be derived by following the same steps. If P_0Q is the vector from some point P_0 on the plane $Ax + By + Cz + D = 0$ to a point $Q(x_1, y_1, z_1)$ off the plane, then the distance d from Q to the plane is the projection of P_0Q onto the normal (A, B, C).

$$d = |\text{Proj}(\overrightarrow{P_0Q} \text{ onto } \vec{n})|$$

$$= \frac{|\overrightarrow{P_0Q} \cdot \vec{n}|}{|\vec{n}|}$$

$$= \frac{|(x_1 - x_0, y_1 - y_0, z_1 - z_0) \cdot (A, B, C)|}{\sqrt{A^2 + B^2 + C^2}}$$

$$= \frac{|A(x_1 - x_0) + B(y_1 - y_0) + C(z_1 - z_0)|}{\sqrt{A^2 + B^2 + C^2}}$$

$$= \frac{|Ax_1 + By_1 + Cz_1 + (-Ax_0 - By_0 - Cz_0)|}{\sqrt{A^2 + B^2 + C^2}}$$

Since P_0 is a point in the plane, it satisfies the equation of the plane, so $Ax_0 + By_0 + Cz_0 + D = 0$ or $D = -Ax_0 - By_0 - Cz_0$. Substituting this into the above equation gives the following result.

> The **distance** from the point (x_1, y_1, z_1) to the plane $Ax + By + Cz + D = 0$ is given by the formula
> $$d = \frac{|Ax_1 + By_1 + Cz_1 + D|}{\sqrt{A^2 + B^2 + C^2}}.$$

Note the structure. The numerator uses the equation of the plane, with the coordinates of the point off the plane substituted for x, y, and z. The denominator is the magnitude of the normal.

In the special case when the point $Q(x_1, y_1, z_1)$ is the origin, the distance to the plane $Ax + By + Cz + D = 0$ is

$$d = \frac{|D|}{\sqrt{A^2 + B^2 + C^2}}.$$

EXAMPLE 4

What is the distance between the planes $2x - y - 2z + 3 = 0$ and $4x - 2y - 4z - 9 = 0$?

Solution
The planes are parallel, since $\vec{n_2} = (4, -2, -4)$ is a multiple of $\vec{n_1} = (2, -1, -2)$. The distance between the planes is the distance from a point in the first plane to the second plane. The point $(0, 3, 0)$ is on the first plane. Then

$$d = \frac{|4(0) - 2(3) - 4(0) - 9|}{\sqrt{(4)^2 + (-2)^2 + (-4)^2}}$$

$$= \frac{|-15|}{\sqrt{36}}$$

$$= \frac{5}{2}$$

Exercise 4.2

Part A

1. For each of the following, find the scalar equation of the plane that passes through the point P_0 and has normal $\vec{n}$.

a. $P_0(2, 1, -3)$, $\vec{n} = (7, 1, -1)$ b. $P_0(5, 1, 9)$, $\vec{n} = (1, 0, 0)$

c. $P_0(0, 6, -2)$, $\vec{n} = (2, 0, 3)$ d. $P_0(0, 0, 0)$, $\vec{n} = (2, -1, 4)$

2. Determine the scalar equation of the plane that passes through $(1, -2, 3)$ and has a normal

   a. parallel to the y-axis

   b. perpendicular to the xy-plane

   c. parallel to the normal of the plane $x - y - 2z + 19 = 0$

3. a. Find the scalar equation of the plane that passes through the origin and has a normal $\vec{n} = (A, B, C)$.

   b. How can you tell by inspection of the scalar equation of a plane whether or not the plane passes through the origin?

4. a. What is the orientation of a plane in space when two of the three variables x, y, and z are missing from its scalar equation?

   b. What is the orientation of a plane in space when only one of the three variables x, y, or z is missing from its scalar equation?

5. Find the scalar equation of each of the following planes. State which of the planes, if any, are coincident.

   a. $\vec{r} = (-8, -1, 8) + s(-5, 1, 4) + t(3, 2, -4)$

   b. $\vec{r} = (-2, -2, 5) + s(3, 1, -1) + t(4, 1, -4)$

   c. $\vec{r} = (2, 0, 0) + s(0, 4, 0) + t(0, 0, -3)$

   d. $\vec{r} = (-8, 2, 0) + s(4, 0, 3) + t(0, -2, -5)$

   e. $\vec{r} = (2, -11, -17) + s(0, 5, 13) + t(0, 3, 10)$

   f. $\vec{r} = (13, 0, -12) + s(-1, 8, -4) + t(11, 3, -12)$

6. Find the scalar equation of each of the following planes.

   a. $x = 4 + 3s - 2t$ b. $x = -2t$

       $y = 2 + 4s + 4t$ $y = 2 - s - 3t$

       $z = 1 - 2s - 3t$ $z = 5 + 3s$

7. For each of the following, find the scalar equation of the plane that passes through the given points.

   a. $(1, 1, -1)$, $(1, 2, 3)$, $(3, -1, 2)$ b. $(2, -2, 4)$, $(1, 1, -4)$, $(3, 1, -6)$

   c. $(1, 1, 1)$, $(-1, 1, 1)$, $(2, 1, 2)$ d. $(1, 3, 0)$, $(0, 5, 2)$, $(3, 4, -2)$

Part B

8. What is the scalar equation of the plane that contains the x-axis and the point $(4, -2, 1)$?

9. Find the scalar equation of the plane that contains the intersecting lines
$$\frac{x-2}{1} = \frac{y}{2} = \frac{z+3}{3} \text{ and } \frac{x-2}{-3} = \frac{y}{4} = \frac{z+3}{2}.$$

10. Determine whether the following pairs of planes are coincident, parallel and distinct, or neither.

 a. $x + 3y - z - 2 = 0$ and $2x + 6y - 2z - 8 = 0$

 b. $2x + y + z - 3 = 0$ and $6x + 2y + 2z - 9 = 0$

 c. $3x - 3y + z - 2 = 0$ and $6x - 6y + 2z - 4 = 0$

 d. $2x - 4y + 2z - 6 = 0$ and $3x - 6y + 3z - 9 = 0$

11. Find a vector equation for the plane with scalar equation

 a. $2x - y + 3z - 24 = 0$ b. $3x - 5z + 15 = 0$

12. Which of the following lines is parallel to the plane $4x + y - z - 10 = 0$? Do any of the lines lie in the plane?

 a. $\vec{r} = (3, 0, 2) + t(1, -2, 2)$

 b. $x = -3t, y = -5 + 2t, z = -10t$

 c. $\frac{x-1}{4} = \frac{y+6}{-1} = \frac{z}{1}$

13. The angle between two planes is defined as the angle between their normals. Determine the angle θ $(0 \le \theta \le 90°)$, to the nearest degree, between the given planes.

 a. $2x + 3y - z + 9 = 0$ and $x + 2y + 4 = 0$

 b. $x - y - z - 1 = 0$ and $2x + 3y - z + 4 = 0$

Part C

14. If the positive z-axis points up, show that the line $x = 0, y = t, z = 2t$

 a. is parallel to and below the plane $2x - 10y + 5z - 1 = 0$

 b. is parallel to and above the plane $x + 4y - 2z - 7 = 0$

15. a. Find an equation for the set of points $P(x, y, z)$ that are equidistant from the points $A(1, 2, 3)$ and $B(4, 0, 1)$.

 b. What does this equation represent geometrically?

16. The vectors $\vec{a}$, $\vec{b}$, and $\vec{c}$ are the position vectors of three points A, B, and C, respectively.

   a. Show that the scalar equation of the plane through A, B, and C can be expressed in the form $(\vec{r} - \vec{a}) \bullet (\vec{a} \times \vec{b} + \vec{b} \times \vec{c} + \vec{c} \times \vec{a}) = 0$.

   b. Find the scalar equation of the plane through the points $A(8, 4, -3)$, $B(5, -6, 1)$, and $C(-4, 1, 2)$.

17. Show that as k varies, the plane $2x + 3y + kz = 0$ rotates about a line through the origin in the xy-coordinate plane. Find parametric equations for this line.

18. When the coefficients A, B, and C in the scalar equation of a plane are the components of a unit normal, what is a geometrical interpretation for the constant D?

19. If a, b, and c are the x-intercept, the y-intercept, and the z-intercept of a plane, respectively, and d is the distance from the origin to the plane, show that

$$\frac{1}{d^2} = \frac{1}{a^2} + \frac{1}{b^2} + \frac{1}{c^2}.$$

20. Find a formula for the scalar equation of a plane in terms of a, b, and c, where a, b, and c are the x-intercept, the y-intercept, and the z-intercept of a plane, respectively.

Section 4.3 — The Intersection of a Line and a Plane

What are the possible ways that a line and a plane in three dimensions can intersect? The line can be parallel to the plane, intersecting it at no points. It can cut through the plane, intersecting it at one point. It can lie in the plane, in which case every point on the line is a point of intersection.

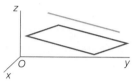
line is parallel to the plane

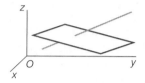
line intersects the plane

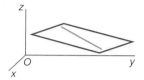
line lies in the plane

EXAMPLE 1

Find the intersection of the line with parametric equations $x = 1 + 2t$, $y = -6 + 3t$, $z = -5 + 2t$ and the plane whose scalar equation is $4x - 2y + z - 19 = 0$.

Solution

In terms of t, the coordinates of a point on the given line are $(x, y, z) = (1 + 2t, -6 + 3t, -5 + 2t)$. This point will lie on the plane if, for some particular value of t, these coordinates satisfy the equation of the plane. Substituting,

$$4(1 + 2t) - 2(-6 + 3t) + (-5 + 2t) - 19 = 0$$
$$4 + 8t + 12 - 6t - 5 + 2t - 19 = 0$$
$$4t - 8 = 0$$
$$t = 2$$

Therefore, the point on the line with parameter $t = 2$ is the point at which the line intersects the plane. Its coordinates are

$$x = 1 + 2(2) = 5$$
$$y = -6 + 3(2) = 0$$
$$z = -5 + 2(2) = -1$$

The point of intersection of the line and the plane is $(5, 0, -1)$.

EXAMPLE 2

Find the intersection of the line $x = 2t$, $y = 1 - t$, $z = -4 + t$ and the plane $x + 4y + 2z - 4 = 0$.

Solution

We find the parameter value of the point of intersection by substituting the point $(2t, 1 - t, -4 + t)$ into the equation of the plane.

$$(2t) + 4(1 - t) + 2(-4 + t) - 4 = 0$$
$$2t + 4 - 4t - 8 + 2t - 4 = 0$$
$$0t = 8$$

There is no value of t which satisfies this equation, so there is no point at which the line intersects the plane.

This means that the line must be parallel to the plane. Its direction vector, $\vec{m} = (2, -1, 1)$, must be perpendicular to the normal to the plane, $(1, 4, 2)$. Indeed,

$$\vec{m} \bullet \vec{n} = (2, -1, 1) \bullet (1, 4, 2)$$
$$= 2 - 4 + 2$$
$$= 0$$

EXAMPLE 3

Find the intersection of the line $x = -4 + 3t$, $y = 0$, $z = t$ and the plane $x - 2y - 3z + 4 = 0$.

Solution

Substitute the point $(-4 + 3t, 0, t)$ into the equation of the plane to find the parameter value of the point of intersection.

$$(-4 + 3t) - 2(0) - 3(t) + 4 = 0$$
$$-4 + 3t - 3t + 4 = 0$$
$$0t = 0$$

In this case, the equation is satisfied for *all* values of t. Therefore, *every* point on the line is an intersection point, and the line lies in the plane.

The intersection of the line and the plane is the entire line itself. You can confirm this conclusion by checking that the particular point $(-4, 0, 0)$ on the line is a point in the plane, and that the direction vector of the line, $(3, 0, 1)$, is perpendicular to the normal to the plane, $(1, -2, -3)$.

The x-, y-, and z-axes are lines in space. The intersections of a plane with these special lines are of particular importance. A plane may intersect an axis at a point, or a plane may be parallel to or contain an axis. These intersections are the key to making sketches of planes in three dimensions.

EXAMPLE 4

Determine the x-, y-, and z-intercepts of the plane $3x - 8y - 8z + 24 = 0$. Make a sketch of the plane.

Solution

To find the *x*-intercept, set *y* and *z* equal to zero.

$$3x - 8(0) - 8(0) + 24 = 0$$
$$3x + 24 = 0$$
$$x = -8$$

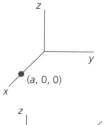

The *x*-intercept of this plane is the point -8. Likewise, the *y*- and *z*-intercepts are 3 and 3, respectively.

Now, plot these on the coordinate axes, join them with straight line segments, and sketch the plane as a *triangular surface*. This figure is a three-dimensional representation of the plane, which extends infinitely in the directions shown by the orientation of the triangle.

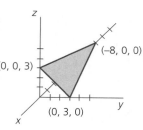

Note that the sides of the triangle formed by the line segments joining the intercepts are segments of the lines in which the plane intersects each of the three coordinate planes.

EXAMPLE 5   Find the intersections of the plane $3x + 2y - 18 = 0$ with the three coordinate axes. Make a sketch of the plane.

Solution

The normal to this plane, $(3, 2, 0)$, has no component in the *z* direction. Therefore, the plane must be parallel to the *z*-axis, and there is no *z*-intercept. By inspection, the *x*- and *y*-intercepts are 6 and 9.

Plot the intercepts. Then, through the intercepts, draw lines parallel to the *z*-axis. The flat region between the parallel lines is a representation of the plane in three dimensions.

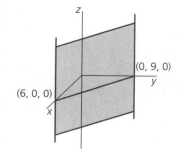

Keep in mind that the plane extends infinitely up and down and left and right, in the directions shown by the orientation of the shaded area. The line joining the intercepts is the line in which the plane intersects the *xy*-plane. The vertical lines through the intercepts are the lines in which the plane intersects the *xz*-plane and the *yz*-plane.

As observed, a plane not only intersects a coordinate axis in a point, but it also intersects a coordinate plane in a line. Clearly, knowing how to find these intersection lines would help us make the sketch of a plane. Fortunately, there is a simple way to find the equations of these lines.

The xy-coordinate plane, for example, is the plane where the z-coordinate of every point is zero. The scalar equation of the xy-plane is $z = 0$. By setting z equal to zero in the equation of a plane, we are singling out those points in the plane that lie in the xy-coordinate plane. These are exactly the points on the intercept line, and by setting $z = 0$ we obtain the equation.

In Example 4, for instance, the plane intersects the xy-coordinate plane in the line $3x - 8y - 8(0) + 24 = 0$ or $3x - 8y + 24 = 0$. In Example 5, the plane intersects the xy-coordinate plane in the line $3x + 2y - 18 = 0$ (there is no variable z in the equation of this plane, so setting z equal to zero does not change the equation).

EXAMPLE 6

Sketch the plane $5x - 2y = 0$.

Solution

Since $D = 0$, the point $(0, 0, 0)$ satisfies the equation of the plane. So this plane contains the origin. Consequently the x- and y-intercepts are both zero. The normal to this plane is $(5, -2, 0)$, so as with Example 5, this plane is parallel to the z-axis. But if the plane is parallel to the z-axis and contains the origin, it must contain the entire z-axis. You can reach the same conclusion by observing that every point $(0, 0, z)$ on the z-axis satisfies the equation of the plane.

The set of planes with this property is illustrated in the given diagram.

Sketch the plane as a parallelogram, with the intersection line and the z-axis as sides. This parallelogram-shaped region represents a section of the plane $5x - 2y = 0$ in three dimensions.

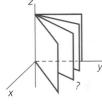

From this set of planes, we choose the one which intercepts the xy-plane along the line with equation $5x - 2y = 0$.

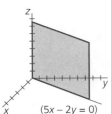

$(5x - 2y = 0)$

Exercise 4.3

Part A

1. For each of the following, find the intersection of the line and the plane.

   a. $x = 4 - t,\ y = 6 + 2t,\ z = -2 + t$ and $2x - y + 6z + 10 = 0$

   b. $x = 3 + 4t,\ y = -2 - 6t,\ z = \frac{1}{2} - 3t$ and $3x + 4y - 7z + 7 = 0$

c. $x = 5 + t, y = 4 + 2t, z = 7 + 2t$ and $2x + 3y - 4z + 7 = 0$

d. $\vec{r} = (2, 14, 1) + t(-1, -1, 1)$ and $3x - y + 2z + 6 = 0$

e. $\vec{r} = (5, 7, 3) + t(0, 1, -1)$ and $z + 5 = 0$

2. a. Does the line $\vec{r} = (-2, 6, 5) + t(3, 2, -1)$ lie in the plane $3x - 4y + z + 25 = 0$?

b. Does the line $\vec{r} = (4, -1, 2) + t(3, 2, -1)$ lie in the plane $3x - 4y + z - 17 = 0$?

3. Where does the plane $3x - 2y - 7z - 6 = 0$ intersect

a. the x-axis?　　　　b. the y-axis?　　　　c. the z-axis?

Part B

4. a. In what point does the plane $\vec{r} = (6, -4, 3) + s(-2, 4, 7) + t(-7, 6, -3)$ intersect

i) the x-axis?　　　　ii) the y-axis?　　　　iii) the z-axis?

b. In what line does this plane intersect the

i) the xy-plane?　　　　ii) the yz-plane?　　　　iii) the xz-plane?

5. Where does the line $\vec{r} = (6, 10, 1) + t(3, 4, -1)$ meet

a. the xy-plane?　　　　b. the xz-plane?　　　　c. the yz-plane?

6. State whether it is possible for the lines and planes described below to intersect in one point, in an infinite number of points, or in no points.

a. a line parallel to the x-axis and a plane perpendicular to the x-axis

b. a line parallel to the y-axis and a plane parallel to the y-axis

c. a line perpendicular to the z-axis and a plane parallel to the z-axis

7. Find the point of intersection of the plane $3x - 2y + 7z - 31 = 0$ with the line that passes through the origin and is perpendicular to the plane.

8. Find the point at which the normal to the plane $4x - 2y + 5z + 18 = 0$ through the point $(6, -2, -2)$ intersects the plane.

9. For each of the following planes, find the x-, y-, and z-intercepts and make a three-dimensional sketch.

a. $12x + 3y + 4z - 12 = 0$　　　　b. $x - 2y - z - 5 = 0$

c. $2x - y + z + 8 = 0$　　　　d. $4x - y + 2z - 16 = 0$

10. For each of the following planes, find the x-, y-, and z-intercepts, if they exist, and the intersections with the coordinate planes. Then make a three-dimensional sketch of the plane.

    a. $x + y - 4 = 0$ b. $x - 3 = 0$ c. $2y + 1 = 0$

    d. $3x + z - 6 = 0$ e. $y - 2z = 0$ f. $x + y - z = 0$

Part C

11. For what values of k will the line $\frac{x - k}{3} = \frac{y + 4}{2} = \frac{z + 6}{1}$ intersect the plane $x - 4y + 5z + 5 = 0$

    a. in a single point?

    b. in an infinite number of points?

    c. in no points?

12. A plane has an x-intercept of a, a y-intercept of b, and a z-intercept of c, none of which is zero. Show that the equation of the plane is $\frac{x}{a} + \frac{y}{b} + \frac{z}{c} = 1$.

Section 4.4 — The Intersection of Two Planes

What are the possible ways two planes can intersect? They can be parallel and distinct, hence not intersecting. They can be coincident, intersecting at every point. They can intersect in a line.

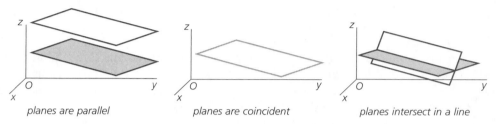

planes are parallel   planes are coincident   planes intersect in a line

If the normals are collinear, the planes are parallel and distinct or coincident. If the normals are not collinear, the planes must intersect in a line.

EXAMPLE 1

Find the intersection of the two planes $2x - 2y + 5z + 10 = 0$ and $2x + y - 4z + 7 = 0$.

Solution

The equations of the two planes constitute a linear system of two equations with three variables.

The normals of the two planes are $(2, -2, 5)$ and $(2, 1, -4)$. These are not collinear, so the planes intersect in a line. To find its equation, we solve the equations.

Subtracting we obtain

$$2x - 2y + 5z + 10 = 0$$
$$2x + y - 4z + 7 = 0$$
$$-3y + 9z + 3 = 0$$

Then $\qquad\qquad\qquad\qquad\qquad y = 1 + 3z$

The value of y depends on the value of z. But there are no constraints on z.

Let $\qquad\qquad\qquad\qquad\qquad z = 2t, t \in R$
Then $\qquad\qquad\qquad\qquad\qquad y = 1 + 6t$

Substituting in equation two,

$$2x + (1 + 6t) - 8t + 7 = 0$$
$$x = -4 + t$$

Parametric equations of the line of intersection of the two planes are $x = -4 + t, y = 1 + 6t, z = 2t$.

The solution of systems of linear equations is such an important topic that several different methods to handle this problem have evolved. One of them makes use of **matrices**. For our purposes, a **matrix** is a rectangular array of numbers made to facilitate the solution of a linear system.

Consider, for instance, the linear system dealt with in Example 1. From the coefficients of x, y, and z in the two equations

$$2x - 2y + 5z = -10$$
$$2x + y - 4z = -7$$

you can form the matrix

$$\begin{bmatrix} 2 & -2 & 5 \\ 2 & 1 & -4 \end{bmatrix}$$

This is a 2×3 matrix – it has two rows and three columns. It is called the **coefficient matrix** of the system. Each coefficient is an **element** of the matrix. The row and column position of each matrix element indicates the equation and the term to which the coefficient belongs.

The constant terms of the equations (which are here written to the right of the equal signs) can be included by adding another column to the coefficient matrix.

$$\begin{bmatrix} 2 & -2 & 5 & -10 \\ 2 & 1 & -4 & -7 \end{bmatrix}$$

This matrix is called the **augmented matrix** of the system. The vertical bar in the matrix shows where the equal signs in the system are located.

The matrix method of solving the system of Example 1 starts with the augmented matrix and proceeds by performing arithmetic operations on its rows. The first operation is to subtract the elements of the second row from those of the first, and then replace the second row with this difference.

$$R_1 - R_2 \qquad \begin{bmatrix} 2 & -2 & 5 & -10 \\ 0 & -3 & 9 & -3 \end{bmatrix}$$

Observe how this operation on the rows of the matrix is expressed in symbolic form: R_1 and R_2 stand for the two rows. By placing $R_1 - R_2$ beside row 2, we indicate where the result is to be placed.

This step is the counterpart of subtracting the equations in Example 1. These operations on the matrix have made the element in the lower left corner equal to zero, which is equivalent to eliminating x in the corresponding equation.

The next step is to divide each of the elements of the second row by -3. We write

$$R_2 \div (-3) \qquad \begin{bmatrix} 2 & -2 & 5 & -10 \\ 0 & 1 & -3 & 1 \end{bmatrix}$$

This is equivalent to the removal of the factor -3 from the result of the subtraction in Example 1.

In order to make the element in row 1, column 2 equal to zero, we multiply the second row by 2, add it to the first row, and replace the first row with this sum.

We write

$$2R_2 + R_1 \qquad \begin{bmatrix} 2 & 0 & -1 & -8 \\ 0 & 1 & -3 & 1 \end{bmatrix}$$

This is equivalent to eliminating y in the first equation. Such operations on the rows of the matrix are legitimate because they match similar operations that could be done on the corresponding equations. Lastly, divide the elements of the first row by 2.

$$R_1 \div 2 \qquad \begin{bmatrix} 1 & 0 & -\frac{1}{2} & -4 \\ 0 & 1 & -3 & 1 \end{bmatrix}$$

At this point the matrix has served its purpose. The two equations corresponding to this matrix are

$$x - \frac{1}{2}z = -4 \qquad \text{or} \qquad x = -4 + \frac{1}{2}z$$
$$y - 3z = 1 \qquad\qquad\qquad y = 1 + 3z$$

Here, x and y are both functions of z, but there are no restrictions on z. So, setting $z = 2t$, the equations of the line of intersection are $x = -4 + t$, $y = 1 + 6t$, $z = 2t$ as before.

The matrix method of solving a system of linear equations, illustrated above, is referred to as **Gauss-Jordan elimination.** A 2×4 matrix of the form

$$\begin{bmatrix} * & * & * & * \\ * & * & * & * \end{bmatrix}$$

can be written down directly from the original equations of the linear system to be solved and then changed into **reduced row-echelon form**

$$\begin{bmatrix} 1 & 0 & * & * \\ 0 & 1 & * & * \end{bmatrix}$$

This form is only one step removed from the solution of the system. The actual operations performed on the rows will depend on what the coefficients are.

The permissible operations that can be performed on the rows of a matrix arise from the algebraic operations that can be performed on the equations of the corresponding linear system.

Row Operations
1. Any row can be multiplied (or divided) by a non-zero constant.
2. Any row can be replaced by the sum (or difference) of that row and a multiple of another row.
3. Any two rows can be interchanged.

Using the matrix methods described above, the solution of a linear system can be systematized so that it can be programmed on a calculator or computer.

This makes it possible to find solutions to systems with many equations and variables, such as those in economics or statistics, which would be difficult, if not impossible, to work out by hand.

The box on page 145 shows how to use a calculator to solve a system of linear equations. If you have a calculator that can perform matrix operations, try using it to work through the example above before continuing.

EXAMPLE 2

Find the intersection of the two planes $4x + 7y - 33z + 17 = 0$ and $-8x - 5y + 3z - 7 = 0$ using Gauss-Jordan elimination.

Solution

The equations of the two planes form the linear system
$$4x + 7y - 33z = -17$$
$$-8x - 5y + 3z = 7$$

The augmented matrix of this linear system is
$$\begin{bmatrix} 4 & 7 & -33 & -17 \\ -8 & -5 & 3 & 7 \end{bmatrix}$$

The solution is achieved by starting with the augmented matrix and carrying out the following row operations to change the matrix into reduced row-echelon form.

$$2R_1 + R_2 \quad \begin{bmatrix} 4 & 7 & -33 & -17 \\ 0 & 9 & -63 & -27 \end{bmatrix}$$

$$R_2 \div 9 \quad \begin{bmatrix} 4 & 7 & -33 & -17 \\ 0 & 1 & -7 & -3 \end{bmatrix}$$

$$R_1 - 7R_2 \quad \begin{bmatrix} 4 & 0 & 16 & 4 \\ 0 & 1 & -7 & -3 \end{bmatrix}$$

$$R_1 \div 4 \quad \begin{bmatrix} 1 & 0 & 4 & 1 \\ 0 & 1 & -7 & -3 \end{bmatrix}$$

The final matrix corresponds to the equations

$$x + 4z = 1 \qquad \text{or} \qquad x = 1 - 4z$$
$$y - 7z = -3 \qquad\qquad\qquad y = -3 + 7z$$

Parametric equations of the line of intersection result when z is set equal to t. They are $x = 1 - 4t$, $y = -3 + 7t$, $z = t$.

EXAMPLE 3

Find the intersection of the two planes $x + 4y - 3z + 6 = 0$ and $2x + 8y - 6z + 11 = 0$.

Solution

The augmented matrix of this system is
$$\begin{bmatrix} 1 & 4 & -3 & -6 \\ 2 & 8 & -6 & -11 \end{bmatrix}$$

The first operation is to put a zero in the lower left corner of the matrix

$$2R_1 - R_2 \qquad \begin{bmatrix} 1 & 4 & -3 & | & -6 \\ 0 & 0 & 0 & | & -1 \end{bmatrix}$$

There is no need to go further. The second row of this matrix corresponds to the equation $0z = -1$, but there is no value of z for which this equation is true. Hence, there is no solution, and the planes do not intersect. They must be parallel. If an elementary row operation makes all the elements of a row zero, this indicates that one equation is a multiple of the other and the planes are coincident. We could say that the normals to the planes, $(1, 4, -3)$ and $(2, 8, -6)$, are collinear, so the planes are parallel and distinct or coincident. Since $(2, 8, -6, 11) \neq 2(1, 4, -3, 6)$, the planes are distinct.

CALCULATOR APPLICATION

Some calculators can put a matrix into reduced row-echelon form and thereby help you to find the solution to a linear system. To solve the linear system of Example 1, for instance, start with the augmented matrix

$$\begin{bmatrix} 4 & 7 & -33 & | & -17 \\ -8 & -5 & 3 & | & 7 \end{bmatrix}$$

and follow the following steps (the instructions are for a TI-83 Plus calculator).

1. To define the matrix,
   press [2nd] [MATRIX], select EDIT, select matrix [A], and press [ENTER].
   To set its dimensions,
   press 2 [ENTER] and 4 [ENTER].
   To enter its elements,
   press 4 [ENTER], then 7 [ENTER], etc., for all eight elements.
   Then press [2nd] [QUIT] to return to the home screen.

2. To put the matrix in reduced row-echelon form,
   press [2nd] [MATRIX], select MATH, then cursor down to **B:rref(**
   and press [ENTER].
   To select which matrix to reduce,
   press [2nd] [MATRIX], select NAMES, select matrix [A],
   and press [ENTER].
   To complete and execute the instruction,
   press [ )] and press [ENTER].

   The result is $\begin{bmatrix} 1 & 0 & 4 & | & 1 \\ 0 & 1 & -7 & | & -3 \end{bmatrix}$

Now write the corresponding equations and complete the solution.

Part A

1. Explain why two planes can never intersect in a single point.

2. Do the following pairs of planes intersect in a straight line?
   a. $-6x + 12y - 9z + 9 = 0$ and $4x - 8y + 6z + 9 = 0$
   b. $2x - y - 2z + 3 = 0$ and $6x - 3y - 6z + 9 = 0$
   c. $\vec{r} = (6, 0, 1) + p(1, 1, 2) + q(4, 2, 3)$
      and $\vec{r} = (1, 1, -9) + s(5, 3, 5) + t(3, 1, 1)$
   d. $\vec{r} = (1, 1, 1) + p(0, 0, 1) + q(0, 1, 0)$
      and $\vec{r} = (0, 0, 0) + s(0, 0, 1) + t(1, 0, 0)$

3. Determine which of the following pairs of planes are parallel. For each pair that is not parallel, find the parametric equations of the line of intersection. Use algebraic elimination.
   a. $x + y - 3z = 4$ and $x + 2y - z = 1$
   b. $5x - 2y + 2z + 1 = 0$ and $5x - 2y + 2z - 3 = 0$
   c. $x - 3y - z + 3 = 0$ and $2x + 4y - z - 5 = 0$
   d. $x + y + z = 1$ and $x = 0$
   e. $x + 3y - z - 4 = 0$ and $2x + 6y - 2z - 8 = 0$

Part B

4. Write the augmented matrix for each of the following linear systems.
   a. $3x - 7y + z = 12$
      $x + y - 2z = -3$
   b. $-4x + 3y + 2z = 4$
      $2y - 5z = 5$
   c. $x + 4z = 16$
      $y - 8z = -2$
   d. $5y - 2z + 6x = 4$
      $3z + 5y - 2x = -4$

5. Write the system of equations that corresponds to each of these matrices.
   a. $\begin{bmatrix} 1 & 0 & 4 & 9 \\ 0 & 1 & -6 & 4 \end{bmatrix}$
   b. $\begin{bmatrix} 8 & -2 & 3 & -6 \\ 2 & -6 & -6 & 9 \end{bmatrix}$
   c. $\begin{bmatrix} 5 & 0 & -10 & 8 \\ 0 & 3 & -4 & 6 \end{bmatrix}$
   d. $\begin{bmatrix} 1 & 0 & 4 & 0 \\ 0 & 1 & 9 & 0 \end{bmatrix}$

6. Use Gauss-Jordan elimination to find the vector equation of the line of intersection of each pair of planes.

a. $x + 2y + 7z = 4$
$x + 3y + 3z = 1$

b. $x - 4y + 3z = 5$
$2x + y + 6z = 0$

c. $2x + 8y + 2z = 7$
$x + 4y - z = 3$

d. $4x - 8y - 3z = 6$
$-3x + 6y + z = -2$

e. $3x + 2y - 6z = 5$
$2x + 3y - 9z = -10$

f. $6x + 8y - 3z = 9$
$10x - 2y - 5z = 15$

Part C

7. What is the geometrical interpretation of the system of equations that corresponds to these matrices?

a. $\begin{bmatrix} 2 & 6 & -2 & 5 \\ 6 & 5 & 1 & -5 \\ 2 & -3 & 4 & 3 \end{bmatrix}$

b. $\begin{bmatrix} -1 & 8 & 5 \\ 4 & 3 & 2 \\ -3 & 2 & -2 \end{bmatrix}$

c. $\begin{bmatrix} 6 & 3 & -4 & 10 \\ 3 & -6 & 4 & 22 \\ 8 & -7 & 1 & 15 \\ 5 & 2 & -5 & -9 \end{bmatrix}$

8. a. Let $A_1x + B_1y + C_1z + D_1 = 0$ and $A_2x + B_2y + C_2z + D_2 = 0$ be two non-parallel planes in space. Show that for any fixed k,

$$(A_1x + B_1y + C_1z + D_1) + k(A_2x + B_2y + C_2z + D_2) = 0$$

is the equation of the plane through the intersection of the two planes. As k varies, this equation generates the family of all such planes (except the second plane itself).

b. Find the scalar equation of the plane that passes through the origin and the line of intersection of the planes $3x + 4y - 7z - 2 = 0$ and $2x + 3y - 4 = 0$.

c. Find the scalar equation of the plane that is parallel to the line $x = 2y = 3z$ and passes through the line of intersection of the planes $4x - 3y - 5z + 10 = 0$ and $4x - y - 3z + 15 = 0$.

9. Find the scalar equation of the plane that is perpendicular to the plane $\vec{r} = (-2, 1, 3) + s(5, -2, -2) + t(-1, 0, 1)$ and intersects it along the line $\vec{r} = (9, -1, -5) + p(2, -2, 2)$.

What are the possible ways three planes can intersect? Before reading further, try to discover as many as you can.

One of the ways that three planes can intersect is in a single point. The three coordinate planes, for instance, intersect in a single point, namely the origin. You can find a point of intersection using algebraic elimination or by using matrices and Gauss-Jordan elimination. Examples 1 and 2 illustrate these methods.

EXAMPLE 1

Find the point of intersection of the three planes using algebraic elimination.

$$① \qquad x - 3y - 2z = -9$$
$$② \qquad 2x - 5y + z = 3$$
$$③ \qquad -3x + 6y + 2z = 8$$

Solution

For these equations, it appears that z is the easiest variable to eliminate.

Add ① and ③

$$x - 3y - 2z = -9$$
$$-3x + 6y + 2z = 8$$
$$④ \qquad -2x + 3y = -1$$

Multiply ② by 2 and add to ①

$$x - 3y - 2z = -9$$
$$4x - 10y + 2z = 6$$
$$⑤ \qquad 5x - 13y = -3$$

Multiply ④ by 5 and ⑤ by 2 and add

$$-10x + 15y = -5$$
$$10x - 26y = -6$$
$$-11y = -11$$
$$y = 1$$

Substitute $y = 1$ in ⑤

$$5x - 13 = -3$$
$$x = 2$$

Substitute $y = 1$ and $x = 2$ in ②

$$4 - 5 + 2 = 3$$
$$z = 4$$

The planes intersect at $(2, 1, 4)$.

Gauss-Jordan elimination in a case like this consists of putting a matrix

$$\begin{bmatrix} * & * & * & | & * \\ * & * & * & | & * \\ * & * & * & | & * \end{bmatrix} \qquad \text{into the reduced row-echelon form:} \qquad \begin{bmatrix} 1 & 0 & 0 & | & * \\ 0 & 1 & 0 & | & * \\ 0 & 0 & 1 & | & * \end{bmatrix}$$

The equations of the three planes constitute a linear system. The augmented matrix for this system is a 3×4 matrix.

$$\begin{bmatrix} 1 & -3 & -2 & -9 \\ 2 & -5 & 1 & 3 \\ -3 & 6 & 2 & 8 \end{bmatrix}$$

To accomplish this in an orderly manner, consider the elements one at a time in the order indicated by the numbers. For each one, carry out the row operations that will turn that element into zero.

$$\begin{bmatrix} * & \#4 & \#5 & * \\ \#1 & * & \#6 & * \\ \#2 & \#3 & * & * \end{bmatrix}$$

EXAMPLE 2

Find the point of intersection of the three planes of Example 1 using Gauss-Jordan elimination.

① $\qquad x - 3y - 2z = -9$
② $\qquad 2x - 5y + z = 3$
③ $\quad -3x + 6y + 2z = 8$

Solution

Starting with the augmented matrix, the calculations are

$$\begin{bmatrix} 1 & -3 & -2 & -9 \\ 2 & -5 & 1 & 3 \\ -3 & 6 & 2 & 8 \end{bmatrix}$$

$-2R_1 + R_2 \quad \begin{bmatrix} 1 & -3 & -2 & -9 \\ 0 & 1 & 5 & 21 \\ -3 & 6 & 2 & 8 \end{bmatrix}$

$3R_1 + R_3 \quad \begin{bmatrix} 1 & -3 & -2 & -9 \\ 0 & 1 & 5 & 21 \\ 0 & -3 & -4 & -19 \end{bmatrix}$

$3R_2 + R_3 \quad \begin{bmatrix} 1 & -3 & -2 & -9 \\ 0 & 1 & 5 & 21 \\ 0 & 0 & 11 & 44 \end{bmatrix}$

$R_3 \div 11 \quad \begin{bmatrix} 1 & -3 & -2 & -9 \\ 0 & 1 & 5 & 21 \\ 0 & 0 & 1 & 4 \end{bmatrix}$

$3R_2 + R_1 \quad \begin{bmatrix} 1 & 0 & 13 & 54 \\ 0 & 1 & 5 & 21 \\ 0 & 0 & 1 & 4 \end{bmatrix}$

$-13R_3 + R_1 \quad \begin{bmatrix} 1 & 0 & 0 & 2 \\ 0 & 1 & 5 & 21 \\ 0 & 0 & 1 & 4 \end{bmatrix}$

$-5R_3 + R_2 \quad \begin{bmatrix} 1 & 0 & 0 & 2 \\ 0 & 1 & 0 & 1 \\ 0 & 0 & 1 & 4 \end{bmatrix}$

The final matrix corresponds to the equations $x = 2$, $y = 1$, $z = 4$. Therefore, the solution is $(2, 1, 4)$, as before.

As you can see from Example 2, it can be a complicated and lengthy process to work out a problem by hand using Gauss-Jordan elimination. Using a calculator with matrix functions makes the work faster and easier (see the box on page 153). Try solving the problem in Example 2 using a calculator.

When working without a calculator, it is usually simpler to do **Gaussian elimination**. This consists of using matrix methods to get just the three zeros in the lower left corner; that is, putting the augmented matrix in row-echelon form.

$$\begin{bmatrix} * & * & * & | & * \\ 0 & * & * & | & * \\ 0 & 0 & * & | & * \end{bmatrix}$$
which in Example 2 is
$$\begin{bmatrix} 1 & -3 & -2 & | & -9 \\ 0 & 1 & 5 & | & 21 \\ 0 & 0 & 11 & | & 44 \end{bmatrix}$$

Then, continue by writing the corresponding equations,
$$x - 3y - 2z = -9$$
$$y + 5z = 21$$
$$11z = 44$$

and finally finish the problem by doing the substitutions as in Example 1. The remaining examples in this section illustrate this method of solving a linear system.

Now that you have the tools to solve systems of three linear equations, it is time to return to the question that started this section: What are the possible ways three planes can intersect?

To answer this question, consider the normals of the three planes.

When the normals of all three are parallel, the possibilities are

3 planes are
parallel and distinct;
no intersection

2 planes are coincident,
the other parallel;
no intersection

3 planes are coincident;
intersection: a plane

When only two of the normals of the planes are parallel, the possibilities are

two planes are
parallel and distinct,
the other crossing;
no common intersection

two planes are coincident,
the other crossing;
intersection: a line

When none of the normals are parallel, the possibilities are

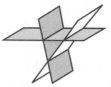

normals coplanar;
no intersection

normals coplanar;
intersection: a line

normals are not parallel
and non-coplanar;
intersection: a point

EXAMPLE 3

Find the intersection of the following planes using Gaussian elimination.

$$x + y + 2z = -2$$
$$3x - y + 14z = 6$$
$$x + 2y = -5$$

Solution
By inspection, none of the normals are collinear. Solving,

$$\begin{bmatrix} 1 & 1 & 2 & | & -2 \\ 3 & -1 & 14 & | & 6 \\ 1 & 2 & 0 & | & -5 \end{bmatrix}$$

$$\begin{matrix} 3R_1 - R_2 \\ R_1 - R_3 \end{matrix} \begin{bmatrix} 1 & 1 & 2 & | & -2 \\ 0 & 4 & -8 & | & -12 \\ 0 & -1 & 2 & | & 3 \end{bmatrix}$$

$$R_2 \div 4 \begin{bmatrix} 1 & 1 & 2 & | & -2 \\ 0 & 1 & -2 & | & -3 \\ 0 & -1 & 2 & | & 3 \end{bmatrix}$$

$$R_2 + R_3 \begin{bmatrix} 1 & 1 & 2 & | & -2 \\ 0 & 1 & -2 & | & -3 \\ 0 & 0 & 0 & | & 0 \end{bmatrix}$$

The corresponding equations are

$$x + y + 2z = -2$$
$$y - 2z = -3$$
$$0z = 0$$

Since the third equation is true for any value of z, set $z = t$, and then solve for x and y in terms of t.

$$y = -3 + 2t$$
$$\text{and} \quad x + (-3 + 2t) + 2t = -2$$
$$x = 1 - 4t$$

The solution is then

$$x = 1 - 4t, y = -3 + 2t, z = t$$

The three planes, none of which are parallel, intersect in a single line, as shown in the diagram.

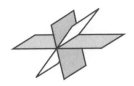

EXAMPLE 4

Determine the intersection of the following planes.

$$x - 2y + 3z = 9$$
$$x + y - z = 4$$
$$2x - 4y + 6z = 5$$

Solution

The normal vectors of the three planes are $\vec{n}_1 = (1, -2, 3)$, $\vec{n}_2 = (1, 1, -1)$, and $\vec{n}_3 = (2, -4, 6)$. Since $\vec{n}_3 = 2\vec{n}_1$, but the third equation is not twice the first, the two corresponding planes are parallel and distinct. The third plane intersects them, as shown in the diagram. Consequently, there is no solution.

Alternatively, using Gaussian elimination, we obtain

$$\begin{bmatrix} 1 & -2 & 3 & | & 9 \\ 1 & 1 & -1 & | & 4 \\ 2 & -4 & 6 & | & 5 \end{bmatrix} \qquad \text{row-echelon form} \qquad \begin{bmatrix} 1 & -2 & 3 & | & 9 \\ 0 & 3 & -4 & | & -5 \\ 0 & 0 & 0 & | & -13 \end{bmatrix}$$

Without proceeding further, we can see that the last row corresponds to the equation $0z = -13$, which has no solution.

EXAMPLE 5

Determine the intersection of the following planes.

$$x - y + 4z = 5$$
$$3x + y + z = -2$$
$$5x - y + 9z = 1$$

Solution

None of the normals are collinear.

$$(\vec{n}_1 \times \vec{n}_2) \cdot \vec{n}_3 = (1, -1, 4) \times (3, 1, 1) \cdot (5, -1, 9)$$
$$= (-5, 11, 4) \cdot (5, -1, 9)$$
$$= 0$$

The normals are coplanar.

$$\begin{bmatrix} 1 & -1 & 4 & | & 5 \\ 3 & 1 & 1 & | & -2 \\ 5 & -1 & 9 & | & 1 \end{bmatrix}$$

$$\begin{array}{c} \\ R_2 - 3R_1 \\ R_3 - 5R_1 \end{array} \begin{bmatrix} 1 & -1 & 4 & | & 5 \\ 0 & 4 & -11 & | & -17 \\ 0 & 4 & -11 & | & -24 \end{bmatrix}$$

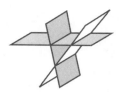

$$\begin{array}{c} \\ \\ R_2 - R_3 \end{array} \begin{bmatrix} 1 & -1 & 4 & | & 5 \\ 0 & 4 & -11 & | & -17 \\ 0 & 0 & 0 & | & 7 \end{bmatrix}$$

The third row corresponds to the equation $0z = 7$, which has no solution. Therefore, the three planes intersect in pairs in three parallel lines, as shown in the diagram.

To check that the lines are indeed parallel, calculate the cross products of the normals:

$$\vec{n}_1 \times \vec{n}_2 = (1, -1, 4) \times (3, 1, 1) = (-5, 11, 4)$$
$$\vec{n}_2 \times \vec{n}_3 = (3, 1, 1) \times (5, -1, 9) = (10, -22, -8)$$
$$\vec{n}_3 \times \vec{n}_1 = (5, -1, 9) \times (1, -1, 4) = (5, -11, -4)$$

The normals are all multiples of the same vector, so this confirms the nature of the intersection.

CALCULATOR APPLICATION

The steps to put a 3×4 matrix into reduced row-echelon form are almost identical to those for a matrix. To solve the linear system of Example 2, for instance, start with the augmented matrix

$$\begin{bmatrix} 1 & -3 & -2 & | & -9 \\ 2 & -5 & 1 & | & 3 \\ -3 & 6 & 2 & | & 8 \end{bmatrix}$$

and carry out the following steps (the instructions are for a TI-83 Plus calculator).

1. To define the matrix,

   press [2nd] [MATRIX], select EDIT, select matrix [A], and press [ENTER].
   To set its dimensions,
   press 3 [ENTER] and 4 [ENTER].
   To enter its elements,
   press 1 [ENTER], then -3 [ENTER], etc., for all 12 elements.
   Then press [2nd] [QUIT] to return to the home screen.

   (continued)

2. To put the matrix in reduced row-echelon form,
   press [2nd] [MATRIX], select MATH, then cursor down to **B:rref(**
   and press [ENTER].
   To select which matrix to reduce,
   press [2nd] [MATRIX], select NAMES, select matrix [A],
   and press [ENTER].
   To complete and execute the instruction,
   press [)] and press [ENTER].

The calculator carries out a Gauss-Jordan elimination.

The result should be $\begin{bmatrix} 1 & 0 & 0 & | & 2 \\ 0 & 1 & 0 & | & 1 \\ 0 & 0 & 1 & | & 4 \end{bmatrix}$. You can read off the solution (2, 1, 4) directly.

Exercise 4.5

Part A

1. Using diagrams, classify the intersections of three planes according to whether the intersection is a point, a line, a plane, or no common points.

2. State whether the normals to the following planes are collinear, coplanar, or neither.

   a. $3x - 4y + 5z = 6$
      $5x - 6y + 7z = 8$
      $6x - 8y + 10z = 9$

   b. $-4x + 9y + 8z = 13$
      $5x + 3y - z = 15$
      $2x + 5y + 2z = -8$

   c. $2x - 2y + z = 6$
      $4x - 2y - 7z = 3$
      $5x - 4y - 2z = 11$

   d. $2x + 2y - 6 = 0$
      $5x + 5y - 8 = 0$
      $3x + 3y - 10 = 0$

3. For each of the following, state the point of intersection of the three planes.

   a. $x - 4 = 0$
      $6y - 3 = 0$
      $2z + 6 = 0$

   b. $x = 0$
      $x + 3y = 6$
      $x + y + z = 2$

   c. $x - y - z = -1$
      $y - 1 = 0$
      $x + 1 = 0$

4. Using algebraic elimination, find the point of intersection of these three planes.

$$x + y + z = -1$$
$$2x + 2y + 3z = -7$$
$$3x - 2y + 7z = 4$$

Part B

5. Write the following linear systems in matrix form.

a. $\quad 5x - 2y + z = 5$
$\quad\ 3x + y - 5z = 12$
$\quad\ x - 5y + 2z = -3$

b. $\quad -2x + y - 3z = 0$
$\quad\ x + 5y = 8$
$\quad\ 3y + 2z = -6$

c. $\quad 4y - 3z = 12$
$\quad\ 2x + 5y = 15$
$\quad\ 4x + 6z = 10$

6. Write the equations that correspond to the following matrices.

a. $\begin{bmatrix} 1 & 0 & 0 & | & 8 \\ 0 & 1 & 0 & | & -6 \\ 0 & 0 & 1 & | & 3 \end{bmatrix}$

b. $\begin{bmatrix} 1 & 0 & -6 & | & 4 \\ 0 & 1 & 5 & | & -5 \\ 0 & 0 & 0 & | & 0 \end{bmatrix}$

c. $\begin{bmatrix} 1 & 0 & 0 & | & 0 \\ 0 & 1 & 0 & | & 0 \\ 0 & 0 & 0 & | & 1 \end{bmatrix}$

7. Using Gaussian elimination, find the point of intersection of these planes.

$$2x - 6y + 4z - 11 = 0$$
$$x - 3y + 4z + 7 = 0$$
$$8x + 18y - 2z + 1 = 0$$

8. Determine the intersection, if any, of each of the following sets of planes. In each case, give a geometrical interpretation of the system of equations and the solution. Also state whether the system has no solutions, a unique solution, or an infinite number of solutions.

a. $\quad x + 2y + z = 12$
$\quad\ 2x - y + z = 5$
$\quad\ 3x + y - 2z = 1$

b. $\quad x - y + 2z = 4$
$\quad\ 2x - 2y + 4z = 7$
$\quad\ 3x - 3y + 6z = 11$

c. $\quad x + y - z = 5$
$\quad\ 2x + 2y - 4z = 6$
$\quad\ x + y - 2z = 3$

d. $\quad -2x + 4y + 6z = -2$
$\quad\ 4x - 8y - 12z = 4$
$\quad\ x - 2y - 3z = 1$

e. $\quad x + y + 2z = 2$
$\quad\ x - y - 2z = 5$
$\quad\ 3x + 3y + 6z = 5$

f. $\quad x + 3y + 5z = 10$
$\quad\ 2x + 6y + 10z = 18$
$\quad\ x + 3y + 5z = 9$

g. $\quad x - 3y - 2z = 9$
$\quad\ x + 11y + 5z = -5$
$\quad\ 2x + 8y + 3z = 4$

h. $\quad x + y + 2z = 6$
$\quad\ x - y - 4z = -2$
$\quad\ 3x + 5y + 12z = 27$

i. $\quad 2x + y + z = 0$
$\quad\ x - 2y - 3z = 0$
$\quad\ 3x + 2y + 4z = 0$

Part C

9. For what value of k will the following set of planes intersect in a line?

$$x - 2y - z = 0$$
$$x + 9y - 5z = 0$$
$$kx - y + z = 0$$

Key Concepts Review

In this chapter, the vector methods used to find the equations of a line have been extended to planes. The resulting equations of a plane are

the **vector equation**

$$(x, y, z) = (x_0, y_0, z_0) + s(a_1, a_2, a_3) + t(b_1, b_2, b_3)$$

the **parametric equations**

$$x = x_0 + sa_1 + tb_1$$
$$y = y_0 + sa_2 + tb_2$$
$$z = z_0 + sa_3 + tb_3$$

the **scalar equation**

$$Ax + By + Cz + D = 0$$

As with lines, it is essential to memorize these equations and to learn to convert quickly, by inspection when possible, from one form to another.

Make a connection between the algebraic equations and the geometrical position and orientation of a line or plane in space. Draw graphs, diagrams, or sketches to increase your ability to visualize intersections.

Finally, try to invest your solutions to problems with meaning. Look at the equations or numerical values of your answers and ask if they answer the question asked, whether are they consistent, and whether they meet your expectations. In a summary statement, express the solution in words.

Like so many astronomers before us and throughout history, we shall determine, through calculations, the angle of elevation of the sun for any given time of any given day at any given place on the surface of the earth.

Investigate and Apply

Let d be the number of days past December 21. Let h be the number of hours (positive or negative) from noon, and let θ be the latitude of the observer.

As previously noted, the vector from the earth to the sun is

$$\vec{s} = \left(150\sin\left(\tfrac{360d}{365}\right),\ -150\cos\left(\tfrac{360d}{365}\right),\ 0\right).$$

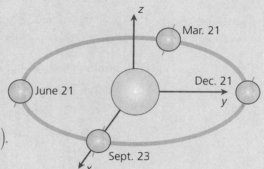

We want to find the angle between $\vec{s}$ and the observer's plane of tangency to the earth. To do this, we will need the normal, $\vec{n}$, of this plane of tangency.

Pick specific values of d, h, and θ (perhaps the current date and time and your current latitude θ). Use negative values of θ for southern latitudes. Calculate $\vec{s}$.

1. Now to find $\vec{n}$ we start by assuming the earth's axis is not tilted.
   a) Given that $\vec{s} = (s_1, s_2, 0)$, let $\vec{n}_1 = s\cos\left(\tfrac{360h}{24}\right) + (-s_2, s_1, 0)\sin\left(\tfrac{360h}{24}\right)$. Why is this the correct normal for a person on the equator?
   b) Let $\vec{n}_2 = \vec{n}_1\cos\theta + (0, 0, |\vec{n}_1|\sin\theta)$. What does $\vec{n}_2$ represent?
2. The earth's axis is tilted $\phi = 23.45°$ away from the z-axis in the direction of the y-axis. If $\vec{n}_2 = (a, b, c)$, then $\vec{n} = (a, b\cos\phi + c\sin\phi,\ c\cos\phi - b\sin\phi)$. Justify this and then calculate $\vec{n}$.
3. a) Let β be the angle between $\vec{s}$ and $\vec{n}$.
   b) Calculate $\alpha = 90° - \beta$. This is the angle of elevation of the sun.
   c) Why is α the angle of elevation of the sun, and not β?
4. What does it mean if the angle of elevation is negative? (In practice, the angle between a line and a plane will always be between 0° and 90°. Why?)

INDEPENDENT STUDY

Develop a general formula for α in terms of d, h, and θ.

How can we find the positions of the stars and the other planets? ●

Review Exercise

1. a. Can a plane be perpendicular to the x-axis and contain the line
   $x = z$, $y = 0$? Explain.

   b. Can a plane be parallel to the yz-coordinate plane and contain the point
   $(-4, 0, 5)$? Explain.

2. Find vector and parametric equations of the plane

   a. that passes through the point $(-1, -1, 2)$ and is parallel to the plane
   $\vec{r} = (2, -1, 0) + s(5, 4, 2) + t(0, 0, 1)$

   b. that passes through the points $(1, 1, 0)$ and $(-2, 0, 3)$ and is parallel to the
   y-axis

   c. that has intercepts $x = -2$, $y = -3$, and $z = 4$

   d. that contains the point $(1, 1, 1)$ and the line $\frac{x}{3} = \frac{y}{4} = \frac{z}{5}$

   e. that contains the two intersecting lines
   $\vec{r} = (3, -1, 2) + s(4, 0, 1)$ and $\vec{r} = (3, -1, 2) + t(4, 0, 2)$

3. Find the scalar equation for the plane

   a. that passes through the point $(1, 7, 9)$ and has normal $\vec{n} = (1, 3, 5)$

   b. that passes through the points $(3, 2, 3)$, $(-4, 1, 2)$, and $(-1, 3, 2)$

   c. that passes through the point $(0, 0, 6)$ and is parallel to the plane $y + z = 5$

   d. that contains the point $(3, -3, 0)$ and the line $x = 2$, $y = 3 + t$,
   $z = -4 - 2t$

   e. that contains the line $\vec{r} = (2, 1, 7) + s(0, 1, 0)$ and is parallel to the line
   $\vec{r} = (3, 0, 4) + t(2, -1, 0)$

   f. that contains the points $(6, 1, 0)$ and $(3, 0, 2)$, and is parallel to the z-axis

4. For what value of k, if any, will the planes $3x + ky + z - 6 = 0$ and
   $6x + (1 - k)y + 2z - 9 = 0$ be

   a. parallel?　　　　　　　　　　　　　　　　b. perpendicular?

5. Find the scalar equation of the plane that contains the parallel and distinct lines
   $x = 1, \frac{y - 3}{4} = \frac{z}{2}$ and $x = 5, \frac{y + 5}{2} = \frac{z - 3}{1}$.

6. Find a vector equation of the plane that contains the origin and the point $(2, -3, 2)$ and is perpendicular to the plane $x + 2y - z + 3 = 0$.

7. Find the scalar equation of the plane that passes through the point $(1, 2, 3)$ and is parallel to the vectors $6\hat{k}$ and $\hat{i} + 2\hat{j} - 3\hat{k}$.

8. A line that passes through the origin intersects a plane at the point $(1, -3, 2)$. If the line is perpendicular to the plane, find the scalar equation of the plane.

9. Find the scalar equation of the plane that contains the intersecting lines $\dfrac{x - 1}{2} = \dfrac{y - 1}{3} = \dfrac{z - 1}{-1}$ and $\dfrac{x - 1}{-1} = \dfrac{y - 1}{5} = \dfrac{z - 1}{4}$.

10. Explain why the point $(2, 21, 8)$ and the line $\vec{r} = (-4, -3, -1) + t(2, 8, 3)$ do not determine a plane.

11. Find the distance between
    a. the point $(7, 7, -7)$ and the plane $6y - z + 5 = 0$
    b. the point $(3, 2, 1)$ and the plane $3x + 2y + z = 10$
    c. the line $\vec{r} = (1, 3, 2) + t(1, 2, -1)$ and the plane $y + 2z = 5$
    d. the planes $x + 2y - 5z - 10 = 0$ and $2x + 4y - 10z - 17 = 0$

12. Find the distance from the point $(1, -2, -2)$ to the plane having an x-intercept of -1, a y-intercept of 2, and a z-intercept of 3.

13. A normal to the plane $4x - 2y + 5z - 9 = 0$ passes through the origin. At what point does this normal intersect the plane?

14. Determine where the plane $4x + 5y - z + 20 = 0$ meets the coordinate axes, and graph the plane.

15. Graph the following planes in an xyz-coordinate system.
    a. $2x + y + z - 3 = 0$ b. $3y - 4z + 24 = 0$
    c. $3z + 9 = 0$ d. $\vec{r} = (4, -5, 0) + s(-12, 9, 8) + t(8, -7, -8)$

16. Show that the line $x = -5 - 3t, y = 3 - 4t, z = 1 + 5t$ lies in the plane $2x + y + 2z + 5 = 0$.

17. For what values of k will the planes $2x - 6y + 4z + 3 = 0$ and $3x - 9y + 6z + k = 0$
    a. not intersect?   b. intersect in a line?   c. intersect in a plane?

18. A plane passes through the points $(1, 0, 2)$ and $(-1, 1, 0)$ and is parallel to the vector $(-1, 1, 1)$.

   a. Find the scalar equation of the plane.

   b. Find the equation of the line through the point $Q(0, 3, 3)$ that is perpendicular to the plane.

   c. Find the point at which the perpendicular through Q intersects the plane.

   d. Use a distance formula to check your answer to part **c**.

19. Find the equation of the plane that passes through the point $(3, 0, -4)$ and is perpendicular to the line of intersection of the planes $x + 2y - 7z - 3 = 0$ and $x - 5y + 4z - 1 = 0$.

20. Let l be the line of intersection of the two planes $x + y + z - 1 = 0$ and $2x - 3y - z + 2 = 0$.

   a. Find the scalar equation of the plane that contains the line l and passes through the origin.

   b. Show that the plane found in part **a** makes an angle of $60°$ with the plane $x - z = 0$.

21. Are the two planes $\vec{r} = (4, 0, 3) + t(-8, 1, -9) + u(-1, 5, 7)$ and $\vec{r} = (-14, 12, -1) + p(1, 1, 3) + q(-2, 1, -1)$ parallel, coincident, or neither?

22. Solve each of the following systems of equations. Give a geometrical interpretation of each system and its solution.

   a. $x + 5y - 8 = 0$
       $5x - 7y + 8 = 0$

   b. $2x - 2y + 4z = 5$
       $x - y + 2z = 2$

   c. $3x + 2y - 4z + 1 = 0$
       $2x - y - z + 3 = 0$

   d. $x + 2y - 3z = 11$
       $2x + y = 7$
       $3x + 6y - 8z = 32$

   e. $x - y + 3z = 4$
       $x + y + 2z = 2$
       $3x + y + 7z = 9$

   f. $x + 3y + 3z = 8$
       $x - y + 3z = 4$
       $2x + 6y + 6z = 16$

   g. $x + 2y + z = -3$
       $x + 7y + 4z = -13$
       $2x - y - z = 4$

   h. $3x - 3z = 12$
       $2x - 2z = 8$
       $x - z = 4$

   i. $x + y + z = -3$
       $x + 2y + 2z = -4$
       $2x + 2y + 2z = -5$

Chapter 4 Test

1. What can you conclude about the intersection of
   a. two planes, if their normals satisfy $\vec{n}_1 \cdot \vec{n}_2 = 0$?
   b. two planes, if their normals satisfy $\vec{n}_1 \times \vec{n}_2 = 0$?
   c. three planes, if their normals satisfy $\vec{n}_1 \times \vec{n}_2 \cdot \vec{n}_3 = 0$?

2. For each of the following, state whether each line lies in the plane $4x + y - z - 10 = 0$, is parallel to the plane, or intersects the plane at a point. Give your reasons.
   a. $x = -3t, y = -5 + 2t, z = -10t$
   b. $\dfrac{x - 2}{4} = \dfrac{y - 2}{1} = \dfrac{z}{-1}$

3. Describe with diagrams all the ways that three planes can intersect in one or more common points.

4. The plane $\vec{r} = (0, 0, 5) + s(4, 1, 0) + t(2, 0, 2)$
   a. intersects the x-axis at what point?
   b. intersects the xz-coordinate plane in what line?

5. Find the scalar equation of the plane containing the line $x = y, z = 0$ and the point $(2, -5, -4)$.

6. Solve the following system of equations and give a geometrical interpretation of the result.

$$x + 2y + z + 3 = 0$$
$$x + 7y + 4z + 13 = 0$$
$$2x - y - z - 4 = 0$$

7. a. Find the distance from the origin to the plane $3x + 2y - z - 14 = 0$.

   b. Find the distance from the point $P(10, 10, 10)$ to the plane $3x + 2y - z - 14 = 0$.

   c. Is P on the same side of the plane as the origin? Give evidence to support your answer.

Random numbers are used for computer simulations of processes that can be modelled using probability. For example, airlines often sell more seats than exist on a plane because they know that some ticket holders may not show up. Of course, if too many tickets are sold, then the airline will have to provide costly incentives to convince some of the extra passengers to wait for the next flight. Using random numbers as part of a model, the airline can simulate different seat-selling strategies without ever trying one in practice. This is the advantage of simulation.

Your calculator has a function that can generate random numbers, usually between 0 and 1, or random digits within a specified range. How does this work? One way to produce a sequence of random digits from the set {0, 1, 2, ..., 9} is to put 10 identical balls numbered 0 to 9 into a container and shake it vigorously. Then, without looking, reach into the container and choose a ball. Note the digit on the ball you selected, replace the ball in the container, and repeat the process. You might get a sequence such as 7, 5, 4, 0, 5, 2, 2, 8, 1.

Here is a sequence of random digits produced by a TI-83. Use the key strokes $\boxed{\text{MATH}} \to \to \to$ PRB 5 to get to the function **randInt(**. Then enter 0, 9, 8,) $\boxed{\text{ENTER}}$ to get the 8 random digits 9, 2, 3, 0, 9, 1, 0, 5. Of course, if you try this you will get a different answer!

How does the calculator produce this sequence since there is no one inside to shake up a container of balls? The answer is that the calculator uses an algorithm that is completely deterministic. The numbers produced will be exactly the same every time if you start with the same initial conditions. This is not true with the container of balls. Hence, the numbers generated by the calculator are far from random. However, the sequence shares many properties with a sequence of random numbers and, if the algorithm is well selected, the numbers produced are good enough for practical purposes.

To see how the calculator generates a sequence of random numbers, we must look (perhaps suprisingly) at how division works. When we divide 37 by 8, the remainder is 5. That is, $37 = 4 \times 8 + 5$. If we divide any integer by 8, we get a remainder of 0, 1, 2, ... or 7. Generally, if we divide any integer x by the integer m, the remainder r is an integer between 0 and $m - 1$, inclusive. We use a fancy notation $x \equiv r\text{mod}(m)$ and say that x is congruent to $r$modulo m". For example, $37 \equiv 5 \text{ mod}(8)$ and $63 \equiv 7 \text{ mod}(8)$. Spreadsheet programs such as EXCEL have a function **mod(x, m)** that returns the remainder when x is divided by m.

One algorithm for generating a sequence of random numbers is a mathematical equation of the form $xn = ax_{n-1} \bmod(m)$, $n = 1, 2, \ldots$ where x_0 is a specified number called the *seed*. The seed can be set by the user or determined in some other way (e.g., from the clock inside the calculator). For example, consider the generator $x_n = 8x_{n-1} \bmod(13)$, $n = 1, 2, \ldots$ with seed $x_0 = 1$. If we substitute $n = 1, 2, 3, \ldots$ 12, we get the sequence 8, 5, 12, 1, 8, 5, 12, 1, 8, 5, 12, 1. This sequence does not look very random since it repeats itself every four terms. We say that the sequence has *period* 4. If we change a in the generator to 2 so that the equation is $x_n = 2x_{n-1} \bmod(13)$, $n = 1, 2, \ldots$, we get the sequence 1, 2, 4, 8, 3, 6, 12, 11, 5, 9, 10, 7, 1, which then repeats. This looks better since the period is now 12. Could the period be longer than 12 for any choice of a?

In practice, m and a are selected so that the sequence has a very large period and other good properties. For example, one version of Waterloo MAPLE uses a generator with $m = 10^{12} - 11$, $a = 427419669081$, which produces a sequence with period $10^{12} - 12$ (do not try to check this by hand!). For amusement, you can try the following.

1. Explain why you must get a periodic sequence with this generator (try specific values for a and m first).

2. For $m = 2^3, 2^4, 2^5$, investigate different values of a to determine the longest possible period. Can you guess the answer for 2^e for any integer value of e?

3. Suppose m is a prime, for example $m = 17$. What are the possible periods for various choices of a?

On your calculator, the function **rand** returns a rational number between 0 and 1. Since the remainder x_n is always less than m, the number displayed is $\frac{x_n}{m}$.

Cumulative Review

CHAPTERS 1–4

1. Show that the cross product of two unit vectors is not generally a unit vector.

2. Prove that $(\vec{u} \times \vec{v}) \times \vec{u}$ is perpendicular to $\vec{v}$.

3. The points $A(2, 4)$, $B(0, 0)$, and $C(-2, 1)$ define a triangle in the plane. Find the cosine of $\angle ABC$.

4. Consider the two lines with equations
   $$\frac{x + 8}{1} = \frac{y + 4}{3} = \frac{z - 2}{1} \text{ and } (x, y, z) = (3, 3, 3) + t(4, -1, -1).$$
   a. Show that the lines are perpendicular.
   b. Find the point of intersection of the lines.

5. Determine whether the point $O(0, 0, 0)$ lies on the plane that passes through the three points $P(1, -1, 3)$, $Q(-1, -2, 5)$, and $R(-5, -1, 1)$.

6. Determine the equation in the form $Ax + By + Cz + D = 0$ of the plane that passes through the point $P(6, -1, 1)$, has z-intercept -4, and is parallel to the line $\frac{x + 2}{3} = \frac{y + 1}{3} = \frac{z}{-1}$.

7. Determine a point A on the line with equation $(x, y, z) = (-3, 4, 3) + t(-1, 1, 0)$, and a point B on the line $(x, y, z) = (3, 6, -3) + s(1, 2, -2)$, so that $\overrightarrow{AB}$ is parallel to $\vec{m} = (2, -1, 3)$.

8. The equation $(x - 1)^2 + (y - 2)^2 + (z - 3)^2 = 9$ defines a sphere in three-dimensional space. Find the equation (in the form $Ax + By + Cz + D = 0$) of the plane that is tangent to the sphere at $(2, 4, 5)$, a point at one end of a diameter of the sphere.

9. Determine the intersection of the line $x = -1 + t$, $y = 3 + 2t$, $z = -t$ with each of the following planes:

a. $x - y - z + 2 = 0$

b. $-4x + y - 2z - 7 = 0$

c. $x + 4y - 3z + 7 = 0$

10. Find the point on the xy-plane that lies on the line of intersection of the planes with equations $4x - 2y - z = 7$ and $x + 2y + 3z = 3$.

11. A plane passes through the points $(2, 0, 2)$, $(2, 1, 1)$, and $(2, 2, 4)$. A line passes through the points $(3, 2, 1)$ and $(1, 3, 4)$. Find the point of intersection of the plane and the line.

12. a. Determine the parametric equations of the line of intersection of the two planes $3x - y + 4z + 6 = 0$ and $x + 2y - z - 5 = 0$.

b. At what points does the line of intersection intersect the three coordinate planes?

c. Determine the distance between the xy-intercept and the xz-intercept.

13. The point Q is the reflection of $P(-7, -3, 0)$ in the plane with equation $3x - y + z = 12$. Determine the coordinates of Q.

14. Determine the components of a vector of length 44 that lies on the line of intersection of the planes with equations $3x - 4y + 9z = 0$ and $2y - 9z = 0$.

15. The line through a point $P(a, 0, a)$ with direction vector $(-1, 2, -1)$ intersects the plane $3x + 5y + 2z = 0$ at point Q. The line through P with direction vector $(-3, 2, -1)$ intersects the plane at point R. For what choice of a is the distance between Q and R equal to 3?

16. Consider two lines

$L_1: (x, y, z) = (2, 0, 0) + t(1, 2, -1)$

$L_2: (x, y, z) = (3, 2, 3) + s(a, b, 1)$

where s and t are real numbers. Find a relationship between a and b (independent of s and t) that ensures that L_1 and L_2 intersect.

17. Determine all values of x, y, and z satisfying the following system of equations.

$$x + 2y - 3z = 1$$
$$2x + 5y + 4z = 1$$
$$3x + 6y - z = 3$$

18. In the following system of equations, k is a real number.

$$-2x + y + z = k + 1$$
$$kx + z = 0$$
$$y + kz = 0$$

a. For what value(s) of k does the system

i) have no solution?

ii) have exactly one solution?

iii) have an infinite number of solutions?

b. For part **a iii**, determine the solution set and give a geometric interpretation.

Glossary

Absolute Value: the positive value of a real number, disregarding the sign. Written as $|x|$. For example, $|3| = 3$, $|-4| = 4$, and $|0| = 0$.

Acceleration: the rate of change of velocity with respect to time.

Algebraic Equation: an equation of the form $f(x) = 0$ where f is a polynomial algebraic function and only algebraic operations are required to solve it.

Angle: given two intersecting lines or line segments, the amount of rotation about the point of intersection (the vertex) required to bring one into correspondence with the other.

Angle of Inclination (of a line): the angle α, $0 \le \alpha \le 2\pi$, that a line makes with the positive x-axis. Also known as the angle of slope or gradient of a line.

Augmented Matrix: a matrix made up of the coefficient matrix and one additional column containing the constant terms of the equations to be solved.

Axis: a line drawn for reference in a coordinate system. Also, a line drawn through the centre of a figure.

Basis Vectors: a set of linearly independent vectors such that every vector in that vector space can be expressed as some linear combination of the basis vectors. In the Cartesian coordinate system, the basis vectors $\hat{i}, \hat{j}$, and $\hat{k}$ form a basis for the two- or three-dimensional spaces in which vectors exist.

Cartesian Coordinate System: a reference system in two-dimensional space, consisting of two axes at right angles, or three-dimensional space (three axes) in which any point in the plane is located by its displacements from these fixed lines (axes). The origin is the common point from which each displacement is measured. In two-dimensional space, a set of two numbers or coordinates is required to uniquely define a position; in three-dimensional space, three coordinates are required.

Cartesian (Scalar) Equation of a Line: an equation of the form $Ax + By + C = 0$ where the vector $\overrightarrow{(A, B)}$ is a normal to the line. There is no Cartesian Equation of a line in three-dimensional space.

Cartesian (Scalar) Equation of a Plane: an equation of the form $Ax + By + Cz + D = 0$ where the vector $\overrightarrow{(A, B, C)}$ is normal to the plane.

Centroid: the centre of mass of a figure. The centroid of a triangle is the point of intersection of the three medians.

Clockwise Rotation: a rotation in the same direction as the movement of the hands of a clock.

Coefficient Matrix: a matrix whose elements are the coefficients of the unknown terms in the equations to be solved by matrix methods.

Collinear: lying in the same straight line. Two vectors are said to be collinear if and only if it is possible to find a non-zero scalar, a, such that $\vec{x} = a\vec{u}$.

Commutative: the property that, for certain binary mathematical operations, the order does not matter. Addition and multiplication are commutative operations.

Concurrency: the condition where lines meet together at a common point. In a triangle, each of the medians, altitudes, angle bisectors, and perpendicular bisectors of the sides are concurrent.

Consistent: a linear system is said to be consistent if it has at least one solution. If there are no solutions, the system is said to be inconsistent.

Coordinate System: a frame of reference used for describing the position of points in space. See *Cartesian Coordinate System.*

Coordinates: a set of numbers that uniquely define the position of a point with respect to a frame of reference. Two coordinates are required in two-dimensional space; three in three-dimensional space.

Coplanar: points or lines lying in a plane are said to be coplanar. Three points uniquely define a plane.

Cosine Law: a formula relating the lengths of the three sides of a triangle and the cosine of any angle in the triangle. If a, b, and c are the lengths of the sides and A is the magnitude of the angle opposite a, then $a^2 = b^2 + c^2 - 2bc \cos A$. Two other symmetrical formulas exist involving expressions for the other two sides.

Counterclockwise Rotation: a rotation in the opposite direction of the movement of the hands of a clock.

Cross Product (Vector): a vector quantity that is perpendicular to each of two other vectors and is defined only in three-dimensional space.

Cube: the three-dimensional Platonic solid that is also called a hexahedron. The cube is composed of six square faces that meet each other at right angles, and has eight vertices and 12 edges.

Degree: the unit of angle measure defined such that an entire rotation is 360°. The degree likely derives from the Babylonian year, which was composed of 360 days (12 months of 30 days each). The degree is subdivided into 60 minutes per degree and 60 seconds per minute since the Babylonians used a base 60 number system.

Direction Angles (of a vector): the angles that a vector makes with the x-, y-, and z-axes, respectively, where the angles lie between 0° and 180°.

Direction Cosines (of a vector): the cosines of the direction angles of a vector.

Direction Numbers (of a line): the components of the direction vector of a line. If the direction vector is normalized into a unit vector, the resulting components represent the direction cosines of the line.

Direction Vector (of a line): a vector that determines the direction of a particular line.

Discriminant: in the quadratic formula, the value under the square root sign: $b^2 - 4ac$. It is used to determine the nature of the roots of an equation.

Displacement: a translation from one position to another, without consideration of any intervening positions. The minimal distance between two points.

Distance: the separation of two points measured in units of length, or the length of the path taken between two points, not necessarily the minimal distance (displacement).

Dot (Scalar) Product: the multiplication of two vectors resulting in a scalar quantity. It is calculated by multiplying the magnitude of each of the two vectors by the cosine of the angle between the vectors with the tails of the two vectors joined together.

Element of a Set: any member of the set.

Equilibrant Force: a force equal in magnitude but acting in the opposite direction to the resultant force. It exactly counterbalances the resultant force, resulting in a state of equilibrium.

Equilibrium, State of: a state of rest or uniform motion of an object that will continue unless the object is compelled to change position by the action of an outside force.

Equivalent: equal in value.

Force: a physical influence that causes a change in the direction of a physical object.

Formula: a mathematical equation relating two or more quantities.

Gauss-Jordan Elimination: a matrix method used to solve a system of linear equations, in which all elements on the main diagonal are made 1, and other elements above or below the main diagonal are made 0 using row reduction.

Gaussian Elimination: a matrix method used to solve a system of linear equations, in which all elements below the main diagonal are made 0 by row reduction, and the resulting lines are considered as equations.

Geometry: the branch of mathematics that deals with the shape, size, and position of figures in space.

Gravity: the force of attraction exerted by one object on another.

Hexagon: a six-sided polygon.

Hypotenuse: the side opposite the right angle in a right-angled triangle. It is always the longest of the three sides.

Hypothesis: a concept that is not yet verified but that, if true, would explain certain facts or phenomena.

Identity: a mathematical statement of equality that is true for all values of the variables. For example, $\sin^2\theta + \cos^2\theta = 1$ is an identity, true for all values of the variable.

Inconsistent: a linear system of equations that has no solution.

Intercept: the directed distance along an axis from the point of origin to a point of intersection of the graph of a curve with that axis.

Lever Arm: the distance along the shaft from the axis of rotation to the point at which the force is applied.

Linear System (of equations): a set of two or more linear equations. A system of linear equations may have a unique solution, an infinite number of solutions, or no solution.

Magnitude: the property of relative size or extent. The magnitude of a vector is the length of the vector from the tail to the head.

Matrix: a rectangular (or square) array of numbers set out in rows and columns. The numbers are called elements. The number of elements is the product of the number of rows multiplied by the number of columns.

Newton's First Law of Motion: an object will remain in a state of rest or equilibrium unless it is compelled to change that state by the action of an external force.

Normal: perpendicular; any vector that is perpendicular to a line is called the normal to the line.

Origin: the point of intersection of the coordinate axes drawn in a Cartesian coordinate system.

Parallel: being everywhere equidistant but not intersecting.

Parallelepiped: a box-like solid, the opposite sides of which are parallel and congruent parallelograms.

Parallelogram: a quadrilateral with opposite sides that are parallel.

Parameter: a variable that permits the description of a relation among other variables (two or more) to be expressed in an indirect manner using that variable.

Parametric Equation: an equation in which the coordinates are each expressed in terms of quantities called parameters (for example, $x = r \cos \theta$, $y = r \sin \theta$ $\theta \geq 0$). θ, the parameter, may assume any positive value.

Perpendicular: a straight line at right angles to another line.

Plane: a flat surface, possessing the property that the line segment joining any two points in the surface lies entirely within the surface.

Polygon: a closed plane figure consisting of n points (vertices) where $n \geq 3$ and corresponding line segments. A polygon of three sides is a triangle; of four sides, a quadrilateral; and so on.

Polyhedron: a solid bounded by plane polygons.

Position Vector: a vector drawn from the origin to the point marking the head of the vector.

Projection: a mapping of a geometric figure formed by dropping a perpendicular from each of the points onto a line or plane.

Pythagorean Theorem: in any right-angled triangle, the square of the hypotenuse is equal to the sum of the squares of the other two sides.

Quadrant: any one of the four areas into which a plane is divided by two orthogonal coordinate axes.

Rectangle: a parallelogram in which the angles are right angles.

Reduced Row-Echelon Form: a matrix derived by the method of Gauss-Jordan elimination that permits the solution of a system of linear equations.

Resultant Force: the single force that has the same net effect of a group of several forces.

Rhombus: a parallelogram having equal sides. The diagonals of a rhombus are at right angles to each other

Scalar: a quantity having magnitude only. Quantities having magnitude and direction are called vectors.

Scalar Dot Product: the multiplication of two vectors resulting in a scalar quantity. It is the multiplication of the magnitude of each of the two vectors by the cosine of the angle between them as they are joined at their tails.

Sine Law: the theorem that relates the lengths of sides of a triangle to the sines of the angles opposite those sides. In a triangle with sides of lengths a, b, and c and angles opposite those sides A, B, and C, $\frac{a}{\sin A} = \frac{b}{\sin B} = \frac{c}{\sin C}$.

Skew Lines: non-intersecting, non-parallel lines in space. Two lines are skew if and only if they do not lie in a common plane.

Slope: the steepness of a line or curve. In the plane, the slope is equal to the tan θ, where θ is the angle of inclination.

Sparse System: a linear system of equations involving a large number of equations, many having coefficients equal to zero.

Speed: the rate of change of distance with respect to time but without reference to direction. The average speed is the distance travelled divided by the travel time. Velocity is the quantity used when direction is indicated.

Sphere: the set of points in space at a given distance (the radius) from a fixed point (the centre). In Cartesian coordinates, the equation of a sphere is $x^2 + y^2 + z^2 = r^2$.

Square: a rectangle having all sides equal.

Symmetric Equation (of a line): the equation of a line determined by eliminating the parameter from the parametric equations of a line.

Symmetry: an attribute of a shape; exact correspondence of form on opposite sides of a dividing line (axis of symmetry) or plane.

Torque: the action of a force that causes an object to turn rather than to change position.

Trigonometric Functions: the sine (sin), cosine (cos), tangent (tan), and their inverses, cosecant (csc), secant (sec), and cotangent (cot). Also called circular functions.

Trigonometry: the study of the properties of trigonometric functions and their applications to various mathematical problems.

Unit Vector: a vector with a magnitude of 1. Such vectors are denoted with a carat [^] sign placed over the symbol. For example, $\hat{i}$, $\hat{j}$, and $\hat{k}$ are unit vectors in the direction of the x-, y-, and z-axes.

Variable: a quantity, represented by an algebraic symbol, that can take on any one of a set of values.

Vector: a quantity possessing magnitude and direction. A directed line segment consisting of two points: the tail (initial point) and the head (end point). The distance between the tail and the head is the *magnitude* of the vector. The *direction* of the vector is the direction of the arrow drawn from the tail to head in reference to the basis vectors of the coordinate system.

Vector Cross Product: a vector quantity that is perpendicular to each of two other vectors and is defined only in three-dimensional space.

Vector Space: an abstract system, first developed by Peano, to enable the study of common properties of many different mathematical objects, including vectors.

Velocity: the distance travelled per unit time where the direction as well as the magnitude (speed) is important.

Velocity (Relative): the velocity of an object that an observer measures when he perceives himself to be stationary (at rest).

Weight: the vertical force exerted by a mass (of a body) as a result of the force of gravitation.

Work: the action of a force on an object causing a displacement of the object from one position to another.

Zero Vector: the zero vector $[\vec{0}]$ has zero magnitude. Its direction is undefined.

Answers

CHAPTER 1

Review of Prerequisite Skills

1. a. $\frac{\sqrt{3}}{2}$ **b.** $\frac{1}{2}$ **c.** $\frac{1}{\sqrt{2}}$ **d.** $-\sqrt{3}$ **e.** $\frac{\sqrt{3}}{2}$ **f.** 1 **2.** $\frac{4}{3}$ **3.** 7.36, 6.78, 50° **4.** 34°, 44°, 102° **5.** 5.8 km **6.** 8.7 km

Exercise 1.1

2. Vector: a, c, g, j, l **3. a.** $\overrightarrow{EF} = \overrightarrow{CB}$ **b.** $\overrightarrow{FE}, \overrightarrow{AD}$ **c.** $\overrightarrow{AB}, \overrightarrow{DE}$
d. $\overrightarrow{AB}, \overrightarrow{BC}$ **e.** $\overrightarrow{FD}, \overrightarrow{EB}$ **5. a.** 45° **b.** 135° **c.** 90° **8. a.** $\overrightarrow{AG}$
b. $\overrightarrow{GF}$ **c.** $\overrightarrow{AF}$ **d.** $\overrightarrow{CA}$ **e.** $\overrightarrow{GA}$ **9. a.** $\overrightarrow{AB} = \overrightarrow{DC}$ **b.** $\overrightarrow{AD} = -\overrightarrow{CB}$
c. $\overrightarrow{BD} = 2\overrightarrow{PD}$ **d.** $\overrightarrow{AP} = \frac{1}{2}\overrightarrow{AC}$ **10.** 10.9° **11.** $|\vec{a}| = 10, 37°;$
$|\vec{b}| = 5, 180°; |\vec{c}| = \sqrt{29}, 112°; |\vec{d}| = 5, 217°; |\vec{e}| = 3, 90°$
12. a. 300 km, N 20° W; 480 km, N 80° E; 520 km SW
b. 1300 km, 5 h 25 min **13.** $-2 < k < 6$

Exercise 1.2

1. a. $\overrightarrow{DB}, \overrightarrow{AC}$ **b.** $\overrightarrow{CA}, \overrightarrow{BD}$ **c.** $\overrightarrow{DK} = \overrightarrow{AD}, \vec{u} + \vec{v} = \overrightarrow{BK}, \overrightarrow{AB}$ **2. a.** $\overrightarrow{BC} +$
$\overrightarrow{CE}, \overrightarrow{BC} + \overrightarrow{CD} + \overrightarrow{DE}, \overrightarrow{BC} + \overrightarrow{CD} + \overrightarrow{DF} + \overrightarrow{FE}$ **b.** $\overrightarrow{BG} - \overrightarrow{EG},$
$\overrightarrow{BC} - \overrightarrow{EC}$ **3. a.** $\overrightarrow{PQ}$ **b.** $\overrightarrow{AG}$ **c.** $\overrightarrow{EC}$ **d.** $\overrightarrow{PR}$ **4. a.** 27.5,
24° to $\vec{v}$ **b.** 11.6, 51° to $\vec{u}$ **5.** 36.5 km, S 54° E **6. a.** 4.4
b. 9.8 **7. a.** $\vec{u} \perp \vec{v}$ **b.** $0° \leq \theta < 90°$ **c.** $90° < \theta \leq 180°$
9. 7.7, 37° to $\vec{a}$ **10. a.** $3\vec{x} + \vec{y}$ **b.** $-2\vec{x} + 4\vec{y}$ **c.** $76\vec{y}$ **d.** $-7\vec{x} + 2\vec{y}$
11. a. $5\hat{i} - 2\hat{j} - \hat{k}$ **b.** $-2\hat{i} - \hat{j} + 12\hat{k}$ **c.** $5\hat{i} - 3\hat{j} - 15\hat{k}$
12. $\vec{x} = \frac{2}{11}\vec{a} + \frac{1}{11}\vec{b}, \vec{y} = \frac{5}{22}\vec{a} - \frac{3}{22}\vec{b}$ **17.** 6, 60° to $\overrightarrow{AB}$
18. 20 **20. a.** $\hat{j} - \hat{k}$ **b.** $\overrightarrow{BH} = \hat{j} + \hat{k}, \overrightarrow{DH} = \hat{i} + \hat{j},$
$\overrightarrow{FE} = -\hat{i} + \hat{j}, \overrightarrow{CH} = \hat{i} + \hat{k}, \overrightarrow{EG} = \hat{i} - \hat{k}$ **c.** $-\hat{i} + \hat{j} + \hat{k}$
d. $\overrightarrow{AH} = \hat{i} + \hat{j} + \hat{k}, \overrightarrow{CF} = \hat{i} - \hat{j} + \hat{k}, \overrightarrow{GD} = -\hat{i} - \hat{j} + \hat{k}$
e. $\sqrt{2}, \sqrt{3}$

Exercise 1.3

2. a. 173.2 N, 100 N **b.** 52.1 N, 15.3 N **c.** 58.3 N, 47.2 N
d. 0 N, 36 N **3. a.** 5 N, W **b.** 13.9 N, N 30° E **c.** 10 N, N 82° W
d. 2 N, NW **4.** 5 N **5.** $\sqrt{|\vec{F_1}|^2 + |\vec{F_2}|^2}, \theta = \tan^{-1}\left(\frac{|\vec{F_1}|}{|\vec{F_2}|}\right)$
6. a. 9.8 N, 15° to 8 N **b.** 11.6 N, 32° to 15 N
7. a. 57.7 N, 146° to 48 N **b.** 25.9 N, 174° to 10 N **9.** 87.9 N, 71.7 N
10. $10\sqrt{3}$ N **11.** b. c. **12.** b. 98° **13.** 911.6 N, 879.3 N
14. 375 N, 0 N **15.** 937.9 N, 396.4 N **16.** $|\vec{u_x}| = 0, |\vec{u_y}| = 5;$
$|\vec{v_x}| \cong 6.9, |\vec{v_y}| \cong 5.8; |\vec{w_x}| \cong 10.9, |\vec{w_y}| \cong 5.1$ **17.** 1420 N
18. a. 92 N, 173 N **19. a.** 108 N **b.** 360 N **20.** 54.5 kN, 7.7 kN
21. 1035 N **22.** 238 N **23.** 19 N, 58°, 38° **24.** 10° off the
starboard bow **25. b.** Yes

Exercise 1.4

1. a. greater, south **b.** greater, north **c.** less, north **d.** less, south
2. a. 60° **b.** not possible **3. a.** 15 km/h south **b.** 77 km/h north
c. 92 km/h north **d.** 77 km/h south **4. a.** 0.6 km **b.** 6 min
5. a. 1383 km **b.** N 13° E **6.** 167 km/h, N 5° W
7. 2.5 m/s, N 56° W **8.** 290 km/h, S 81° E **9. a.** 204 km/h, 66 km/h
10. a. S 25° E **b.** 510 km/h **11.** N 62° E **12.** b **13.** 12 m/s
14. 94.3 km/h, N 32° E

Review Exercise

1. a. $\vec{0}$ **b.** 1 **c.** 0 **5. a.** 5 **b.** 25 **c.** $\sqrt{a^2 + b^2}$ **7. a.** 32 N **b.** 22°
8. a. 79 N **b.** 32 N **9.** 605 N, 513 N **10.** 18 N, 8° with 12 N and
32° with 5 N forces **11.** 94 N, 80 N **12. a.** N 86° E **b.** 1 h 5 min
13. 140 km/h **14. a.** 66 m **b.** 100 s **15. a.** N 69° E **b.** 451 km/h
c. 47 min **16.** 7.9 knots, N 54° E **17.** 320 km, S 70° E
18. $a = k|\vec{v}|, b = k|\vec{u}|, k \in R$ **19.** $\vec{u} = -\vec{v}$

Chapter 1 Test

3. $7\vec{u} + 6\vec{v}$ **4.** distributive property **5.** 12.5 N **6.** 294 N, 392 N
7. 68° upstream to the bank, 2 min 55 sec **8.** 640 knots, S 44° E

CHAPTER 2

Exercise 2.1

2. a. $-5\hat{i} + 2\hat{j}$ **b.** $6\hat{j}$ **c.** $-\hat{i} + 6\hat{j}$ **3. a.** (2, 1) **b.** (−3, 0)
c. (5, −5) **4. a.** $-2\hat{i} + \hat{j} + \hat{k}$ **b.** $3\hat{i} + 4\hat{j} - 3\hat{k}$ **c.** $4\hat{j} - \hat{k}$
d. $-2\hat{i} + 7\hat{k}$ **5. a.** (3, −8, 1) **b.** (−2, −2, −5) **c.** (0, 2, 6)
d. (−4, 9, 0) **6. a.** $(-6\sqrt{2}, 6\sqrt{2})$ **b.** $(18\sqrt{3}, -18)$
c. (−15.8, −2.8) **d.** (0, −13) **7. a.** 12, 150° **b.** $8\sqrt{3}$, 240°
c. 5, 37° **d.** 8, 90° **8. a.** (−4, −3) **b.** (5, −2) **c.** (−5, 0, 6)
d. (4, −7, 0) **e.** (−6, 2, 6) **f.** (11, 12, 3) **10. a.** on the z-axis
b. yz-plane **c.** xz-plane **d.** xy-plane **e.** a line parallel to the
z-axis through (1, 3.0) **f.** a line with $x = y = z$
11. a. xy-plane **b.** x-axis **c.** yz-plane **d.** z-axis **e.** xz-plane
f. y-axis **13. a.** $2\sqrt{5}$, 82° **b.** 6, 270° **c.** 15, 127° **d.** 1, 120°
e. $\sqrt{2}$, 309° **f.** $\sqrt{6}$, 180° **14. a.** 14 **b.** 35.1 **c.** 1 **d.** 4
16. a. $\sqrt{17}$ **b.** $\left(\frac{2}{\sqrt{17}}, \frac{3}{\sqrt{17}}, \frac{-2}{\sqrt{17}}\right)$, yes **17. a.** 7 **b.** $\left(\frac{2}{7}, \frac{-3}{7}, \frac{-6}{7}\right)$
18. $\left(\frac{-3}{13}, \frac{-4}{13}, \frac{-12}{13}\right)$ **20. a.** (5, 9) **b.** (9, −6) **c.** (−5, 6, 0)
d. (4, −9, 11) **22.** 55°, 125° **24.** 7

Exercise 2.2

2. a. (3, 3) **b.** (5, 20) **c.** (0, 0) **d.** (1, −7) **e.** (0, 0, 6)
f. (2, 2, −8) **g.** (6, −2, 0) **h.** (−8, 11, 3) **i.** (0, 2, 5)
j. (4, −6, 8) **k.** (−12, −42, −20) **l.** (21, 6, 32)
3. a. $6\hat{i} - \hat{j}$ **b.** $6\hat{i} - 18\hat{j} + 18\hat{k}$ **c.** $-5\hat{i} + 2\hat{k}$
d. $90\hat{i} - 35\hat{j} - 35\hat{k}$ **4. a.** (1, −10, 14) **b.** (−1, −9, 10)
c. (−5, −15, 16) **d.** (13, 11, 0) **e.** (−5, 8, −15)
f. (6, −18, 29) **5. a.** $6\hat{i} - \hat{j} + 7\hat{k}$ **b.** $2\hat{i} + \hat{j} + 5\hat{k}$
c. $2\hat{i} - 3\hat{j} - 3\hat{k}$ **d.** $-2\hat{i} + 3\hat{j} + 3\hat{k}$ **6. a.** $\sqrt{11}$ **b.** $3\sqrt{3}$
c. $\sqrt{149}$ **7. a.** $5\sqrt{2}$ **b.** $\sqrt{30}$ **c.** (−5, −3, 0) **d.** $\sqrt{34}$
e. (5, 3, 0) **f.** $\sqrt{34}$ **9. a.** $\overrightarrow{AB} \not\parallel \overrightarrow{CD}, |\overrightarrow{AB}| = |\overrightarrow{CD}|$ **b.** $\overrightarrow{AB} \parallel \overrightarrow{CD},$
$|\overrightarrow{AB}| \neq |\overrightarrow{CD}|$ **c.** $\overrightarrow{AB} \parallel \overrightarrow{CD}, |\overrightarrow{AB}| = |\overrightarrow{CD}|$ **10.** (−13, −5)
11. (−3, −7), (−7, 13), (17, −9) **12.** (7, 6, 0), (6, 4, −3),
(5, 10, −1), (9, 10, −2) **13. a.** (4, 3) **b.** $\left(\frac{3}{2}, \frac{-7}{2}\right)$ **c.** (2, 6, 0)
d. $\left(\frac{9}{2}, \frac{9}{2}, -3\right)$ **14. a.** 2, 1 **b.** $-5, \frac{-1}{3}, -20$ **15.** $\left(\frac{6}{7}, \frac{2}{7}, \frac{3}{7}\right)$
16. a. (0, 1, 0) **b.** (1, 0, 2) **17. a.** $\frac{5}{2}$ **b.** $\frac{5}{3}$ **18. a.** $\left(1, \frac{-1}{3}\right)$
b. $\left(\frac{1}{3}, \frac{1}{3}, \frac{1}{3}\right)$ **c.** $\left(\frac{15}{4}, 1\right)$ **d.** $\left(\frac{1}{4}, \frac{1}{4}, \frac{1}{4}\right)$ **19. a.** $\left(\frac{18}{11}, \frac{-41}{11}\right)$
b. $\left(\frac{2}{11}, \frac{-17}{11}, \frac{72}{11}\right)$

Exercise 2.3

1. a. $|\vec{a}||\vec{b}|, 0, -|\vec{a}||\vec{b}|$ **b.** acute, obtuse, $90°$ **2. a.** $6\sqrt{2}$
b. 15 **c.** $\frac{-27\sqrt{2}}{2}$ **d.** 0 **3. a.** 0, perpendicular **b.** -29, not
 perpendicular **c.** 0, perpendicular **d.** -28, not perpendicular
4. a. 0 **b.** -14 **c.** 0 **d.** 25 **e.** 6 **f.** 130, a and c are perpendicular
5. a. $(3, 2), (-6, -4), \left(\frac{3}{13}, \frac{2}{13}\right)$ **b.** 2 **6. a.** $(0, 1, 3), (3, 2, 0),$
$(3, 4, 6)$ **b.** infinite number **7. a.** 0.9931 **b.** -0.1750 **8. a.** $107°$
b. $89°$ **c.** $55°$ **d.** $73°$ **9. a.** -6 **b.** $\frac{106}{3}$ **10.** $(0, 4, -3)$
11. $y = \frac{-4}{3}z - \frac{20}{3}$ **14. a.** -1 **b.** -3 **c.** 17
15. a. $15|\vec{a}|^2 + 38\vec{a} \cdot \vec{b} + 24|\vec{b}|^2$ **b.** $4|\vec{a}|^2 - |\vec{b}|^2$
16. -80 **17.** $60°$ **18. a.** $\frac{-3}{2}$ **b.** $\frac{-11}{2}$ **19.** $\frac{5\sqrt{3}}{2}$, $72°, 108°$
20. a. Pythagorean Theorem
b. $|\vec{c}|^2 = |\vec{a}|^2 + |\vec{b}|^2 - 2|\vec{a}||\vec{b}| \cos\theta$ cosine law
22. $\left(\frac{3}{5}, \frac{4}{5}, 0\right)$ **23.** $\frac{-29}{2}$ **24.** $71°$

Exercise 2.4

2. a. 55.6, into **b.** 389.7, out **c.** 3.1, into **3.** vectors are f, h, i, j;
scalars are a, c, e, k **4. a.** $(0, 1, 0)$ **b.** $(1, 0, -1)$
c. $(-10, 7, 9)$ **d.** $(45, 20, 8)$ **5.** $\left(0, \frac{1}{\sqrt{10}}, \frac{3}{\sqrt{10}}\right)$
6. $(4, 2, 0), (-2, -1, 0)$ **10. a.** 19 **b.** 19 **c.** 19 **d.** $(-5, 1, 21)$
e. $(-1, 2, -23)$ **f.** $(6, -3, 2)$ **15. a.** $-4, 2$ **b.** $(-2, -1, 1)$

Exercise 2.5

1. a. $\left(\frac{48}{13}, \frac{32}{13}\right); \frac{16\sqrt{13}}{13}$ **b.** $\left(\frac{-42}{13}, \frac{28}{13}\right); \frac{14\sqrt{13}}{13}$
c. $\left(\frac{40}{89}, \frac{-30}{89}, \frac{-80}{89}\right); \frac{10\sqrt{89}}{89}$ **d.** $(0, 0, -4); 4$ **3.** $2\hat{i}, 3\hat{j}, -4\hat{k}$
4. $-3\hat{i}, -\hat{j}, \vec{0}$ **5. a.** $\left(\frac{1}{3}, \frac{1}{3}, \frac{1}{3}\right)$ **b.** $(1, 0, 0)$ **6. a.** $\sqrt{65}$ **b.** 0
7. a. $\frac{49}{2}$ **b.** $\frac{\sqrt{3}}{2}$ **8.** 29 **9. a.** 2165 J **b.** 1.0 J **c.** -29 J **d.** 0 J
10. greater than 225 J **11.** 7240 J **12.** 32819 J **13.** 80 J
14. 2114 J **15. a.** 10 **b.** 22 **c.** 46×10^3 **d.** -88 **16.** $60\sqrt{2}$ J
17. $-19\sqrt{30}$ J **18. a.** 5 N **b.** 10 J, $\theta = 90°$

Review Exercise

1. a. $\hat{i} + 3\hat{j} + 2\hat{k}$ **b.** $\hat{i} + 5\hat{k}$ **c.** $-6\hat{i} - 8\hat{j} + 11\hat{k}$
d. $9\hat{i} - 6\hat{j} + 2\hat{k}$ **2. a.** $(3, -2, 7)$ **b.** $(-9, 3, 14)$ **c.** $(1, 1, 0)$
d. $(2, 0, -9)$ **3. a.** -3 **b.** $96°$ **4.** $(-16, 2, 3)$
5. $|\vec{a}|^2 - |\vec{b}|^2$ **6.** $\vec{a} \cdot \vec{c} + \vec{a} \cdot \vec{d} + \vec{b} \cdot \vec{c} + \vec{b} \cdot \vec{d}$ **7.** 4 **8.** 1 **9.** 84
12. b. $\sqrt{82}$ **c.** 16.2 **d.** $(1, 5, 4)$ **13. a.** $17\hat{i}, -3\hat{j}, 8\hat{k}$
b. $(17, -3, 0), (0, -3, 8), (17, 0, 8)$ **14.** 36 **15. a.** $(0, 0, 0),$
$(0, 1, 0), \left(\frac{\sqrt{3}}{2}, \frac{1}{2}, 0\right), \left(\frac{\sqrt{3}}{6}, \frac{1}{2}, \frac{\sqrt{6}}{3}\right)$ **b.** $\left(\frac{\sqrt{3}}{6}, \frac{1}{2}, \frac{\sqrt{6}}{12}\right)$
c. $\frac{\sqrt{6}}{4}$ **17.** $\frac{197}{3}$

Chapter 2 Test

1. a. $\vec{u} \perp \vec{v}$ **b.** $\vec{u} = k\vec{v}, k > 0$ **c.** $\vec{u} = k\vec{v}$ **d.** $\vec{u} \perp \vec{v}$ **e.** nothing **f.** $\vec{u} = k\vec{v}$
2. a. $33\hat{i} + 5\hat{k}$ **b.** -4 **c.** $-5\hat{i} - 12\hat{j} + 33\hat{k}$
d. $\frac{5}{\sqrt{1258}}\hat{i} + \frac{12}{\sqrt{1258}}\hat{j} - \frac{33}{\sqrt{1258}}\hat{k}$ **3. b. ii.** 5 **iii.** $\sqrt{13}$
4. a. $(0, -2, 1)$ **b.** $129°$ **c.** $\sqrt{185}$ **5.** 1562.5 J
6. a. perpendicular to the axis of the wrench **b.** 9 J, perpendicular to
the plane of the wrench and the applied force **c.** $30°$
7. $\frac{|\vec{a}|^2 - |\vec{b}|^2}{|\vec{a}|^2 + |\vec{b}|^2}$ for $|\vec{a}| > |\vec{b}|$

CHAPTER 3

Exercise 3.1

2. a. $(-3, 1)$ **b.** $(4, 5)$ **c.** $(1, 3)$ **d.** $(4, 3)$ **e.** $(1, 0)$ **f.** $(0, 1)$
3. a. $(3, 0), (11, -4)$ **b.** $(4, 0), (4, 10)$
4. a. $x = 2 + 2t, y = t; \vec{r} = (2, 0) + t(2, 1)$
b. $x = 3 - t, y = t; \vec{r} = (3, 0) + t(-1, 1)$
6. a. $x = 1 + t, y = 1 - t; (2, 0), (-2, 4)$ **b.** $x = 5 + t, y = 3t;$
$(6, 3), (3, -6)$ **7. a.** $x = t, y = 0$ **b.** $x = t, y = 5$
8. a. $\vec{r} = (-2, 7) + t(3, -4)$ **b.** $\vec{r} = \left(2, \frac{3}{4}\right) + t(1, 9)$
c. $\vec{r} = (1, -1) + t(-\sqrt{3}, 3)$ **d.** $\vec{r} = (0, 0) + t(-2, 3)$
9. a. $\vec{d} = (3, -1)$ **b.** $\vec{d} = (4, 3); (5, 4)$ **c.** $\vec{d} = (1, -10); (-1, 18)$
10. a. perpendicular **b.** parallel **11.** $\vec{r} = (4, 5) + t(7, -3)$
12. a. $(6, 0)$ **b.** $(-7, 0), (0, 35)$ **c.** $(11, 0), \left(0, \frac{11}{3}\right)$ **13.** $87°$
14. a. (i) $127°$ **(ii)** $11°$ **15. a.** $x = 24 + 85t, y = 96 - 65t$
b. 1 h 12 min **c.** $(126, 18)$ **16. b. (i)** $\frac{x - 5}{-8} = \frac{y + 3}{5}$
(ii) $\frac{x}{4} = \frac{y + 4}{1}$ **c.** $\frac{x - 7}{6} = \frac{y + 2}{1}$ **17. b.** $x = 7 + 2t,$
$y = 3 - 5t, -1 \le t \le 5$ **18. b.** $0 < t < 1$ **d.** $t > \frac{1}{2}$
19. a. $\vec{r} = (5, 2) + t(2, -1); \vec{r} = (5, 2) + s(1, 2)$ **c.** yes

Exercise 3.2

2. a. $(2, 1)$ **b.** $(1, -2)$ **c.** $(2, -1)$ **d.** $(1, 2)$
3. a. $2x + 7y + 6 = 0$ **b.** $2x - 1 = 0$ **c.** $x + y - 6 = 0$
d. $x - y = 0$ **4. a.** $\vec{n} = (4, 3), \vec{d} = (3, -4), P(3, 0)$
b. $\vec{n} = (1, -2); \vec{d} = (2, 1), P\left(\frac{14}{3}, 0\right)$ **c.** $\vec{n} = (1, 0);$
$\vec{d} = (0, 1), P(5, 6)$ **d.** $\vec{n} = (3, -1); \vec{d} = (1, 3), P(2, -4)$
6. a. $x - 4y - 28 = 0$ **b.** $x - 2y + 5 = 0$ **c.** $7x - 2y = 0$
d. $y + 2 = 0$ **7. a.** $2x - 3y - 22 = 0$ **b.** $2x + 3y + 14 = 0$
c. $3x + 2y + 6 = 0$ **d.** $3x - 2y - 18 = 0$
8. $3x + 5y - 14 = 0$ **9. a.** $\vec{r} = (0, 5) + t(3, 5); x = 3t,$
$y = 5t + 5; \frac{x}{3} = \frac{y - 5}{5}$ **b.** $\vec{r} = \left(0, \frac{-3}{2}\right) + t(3, 2); x = 3t,$
$y = 2t - \frac{3}{2}; \frac{x}{3} = \frac{y + \frac{3}{2}}{2}$ **11. a.** $\frac{7}{\sqrt{13}}$ **b.** $\frac{12}{\sqrt{53}}$ **c.** 0 **d.** 8
12. a. $\frac{7\sqrt{5}}{3}$ **b.** $\frac{2\sqrt{5}}{3}$ **c.** $\frac{\sqrt{5}}{3}$ **d.** 0 **14. b.** $153°$
c. $\sqrt{3}x + y + 4 - 6\sqrt{3} = 0$
15. a. $x^2 + y^2 - 10x - 12y + 36 = 0$

Exercise 3.3

2. a. $(4, -2, 5)$ **b.** $(7, -2, 3)$ **c.** $(-1, 2, 4)$
3. a. $(4, 0, 1), (-5, 3, 4)$ **b.** $(4, -2, 5), (2, 3, 9)$
c. $(4, -5, -1), (7, -1, -2)$ **4. a.** $\vec{r} = (2, 4, 6) + t(1, 3, -2);$
$x = 2 + t, y = 4 + 3t, z = 6 - 2t;$
$\frac{x - 2}{1} = \frac{y - 4}{3} = \frac{z - 6}{-2}$
b. $\vec{r} = (0, 0, -5) + t(1, -4, -1); x = t, y = -4t, z = -5 - t;$
$\frac{x}{1} = \frac{y}{-4} = \frac{z + 5}{-1}$ **c.** $\vec{r} = (1, 0, 0) + t(0, 0, -1);$
$x = 1, y = 0, z = -t$ **5.** $(-20, 10, -27), (-14, 8, -17),$
$(-8, 6, -7), (-2, 4, 3), (4, 2, 13), (10, 0, 23), (16, -2, 33)$
6. a. $P(2, 4, 2)$ **b.** $a = -8, b = -1$ **7.** $x = 6t, y = -1 + 4t,$
$z = 1 + t$ **8.** $\frac{x}{6} = \frac{y}{7} = \frac{z}{-2}$ **9. a.** parallel **b.** neither **c.** same
12. $\frac{x + 6}{6} = \frac{y - 4}{-5} = \frac{z - 2}{-2}$ **13. b.** $x = 3t, y = t, z = 2 + 6t;$
$-3 \le t \le 2$ **14.** $\vec{r} = (4, 5, 5) + s(1, 5, 2)$ **15. b.** $\frac{\sqrt{66}}{6}$
c. $\sqrt{\frac{1555}{74}}$

Exercise 3.4

2. a. $(-5, -1)$ **b.** $(1, -2)$ **3. a.** coincident **b.** neither **c.** neither
d. parallel and distinct **4. a.** $(8, 2, 3)$ **b.** lines are coincident
c. skew **d.** parallel and distinct **e.** $(-1, 1, 1)$
5. a. $(-2, -3, 0)$ **b.** $\vec{r} = (-2, -3, 0) + s(1, -2, 1)$ **6.** $(2, 3, 1)$
7. x intercept is -4 **8.** $\left(\dfrac{21}{2}, -1\right)$
11. $\vec{r} = (-5, -4, 2) + t(14, -5, 2)$;
$(9, -9, 4)$ **12.** $(2, -1, -1)$, $(1, 2, 1)$, No
13. $\vec{r} = s(17, -15, -20)$ **14. a.** $\left(\dfrac{-AC}{A^2 + B^2}, \dfrac{-BC}{A^2 + B^2}\right)$
b. $\dfrac{|C|}{\sqrt{A^2 + B^2}}$ **15.** $(0, 1, 2)$, $(1, 1, 1)$ **16. a.** $\sqrt{3}$ **b.** 6

Review Exercise

2. a. $\vec{r} = (3, 9) + t(1, 1)$ **b.** $\vec{r} = (-5, -3) + t(1, 0)$
c. $\vec{r} = (0, -3) + t(2, -5)$ **3. a.** $x = -9 + 3t, y = 8 - 2t$
b. $x = 3 + 2s, y = -2 - 3s$ **c.** $x = 4 + 2t, y = t$
4. a. $\vec{r} = (2, 0, -3) + t(5, -2, -1)$ **b.** $\vec{r} = (-7, 0, 0) + t(7, 4, 0)$
c. $\vec{r} = (0, 6, 0) + t(4, -2, 5)$ **5. a.** $x = 3t, y = 2t, z = -t$
b. $x = 6, y = -4 + t, z = 5$ **c.** $x = t, y = -3t, z = -3 + 6t$
6. a. $3x - 4y - 5 = 0$ **b.** $x + 2y + 1 = 0$ **c.** $4x - y = 0$
7. a. $x = 6 + 5t, y = 4 - 2t, z = -3t$ **b.** $m = 8, n = -2$
8. a. coincident **b.** perpendicular **c.** parallel and distinct
d. neither parallel nor perpendicular **9.** $\left(-3, \dfrac{11}{2}, 0\right)$, $(8, 0, 22)$,
$(0, 4, 6)$ **10. a.** $5x + y - 13 = 0$ **b.** $\vec{r} = (0, 5) + t(2, 5)$
c. $\vec{r} = (2, 2) + t(4, 3)$ **11. a.** $(6, 0, 0)$, $(0, 8, 4)$
b. x intercept is 6 **12. a.** $\cos \alpha = \dfrac{5}{\sqrt{30}}$, $\cos \beta = \dfrac{2}{\sqrt{30}}$,
$\cos \gamma = \dfrac{-1}{\sqrt{30}}$; $\alpha \cong 24°$, $\beta \cong 69°$, $\gamma \cong 101°$
b. $\cos \alpha = \dfrac{8}{9}$, $\cos \beta = \dfrac{-1}{9}$, $\cos \gamma = \dfrac{-4}{9}$; $\alpha \cong 27°$, $\beta \cong 96°$,
$\gamma \cong 116°$ **c.** $\cos \alpha = \dfrac{4}{\sqrt{17}}$, $\cos \beta = \dfrac{1}{\sqrt{17}}$, $\cos \gamma = 0$;
$\alpha \cong 14°$, $\beta \cong 76°$, $\gamma = 90°$ **13. a.** $(0, 0, 2)$ **14. a.** $3\sqrt{5}$
b. $\dfrac{22\sqrt{13}}{13}$ **c.** $\sqrt{2}$ **d.** $\dfrac{5\sqrt{3}}{3}$ **15.** $(4, -1, 5)$

Chapter 3 Test

1. a. $\vec{r} = (9, 2) + t(3, -1)$ **b.** $x = 9 + 3t, y = 2 - t$
c. $\dfrac{x - 9}{3} = \dfrac{y - 2}{-1}$ **d.** $x + 3y - 15 = 0$ **2.** $3x + 2y - 2 = 0$
3. $(-2, 2, 0)$, $(0, 3, -1)$ **4.** $3\sqrt{2}$ **5.** $\vec{r} = (1, -1, \sqrt{2})s$;
$\vec{r} = (-1, -1, \sqrt{2})t$ **6.** $(8, 2, 3)$ **7. b.** $P_1(-10, 1, 2)$
c. $P_2(-1, -2, -3)$

CHAPTER 4

Exercise 4.1

2. a. $(1, 0, 0)$, $(4, 0, -3)$ **b.** y component is 0
3. a. $(-3, 5, 2)$, $(-6, 1, 2)$ **b.** $(5, -5, 3)$, $(1, 6, -2)$
c. $(4, -2, 1)$, $(-1, 5, 2)$ **4. a.** $(9, 4, -3)$, $(7, 4, 4)$
b. $(1, 1, 2)$, $(1, 1, -2)$ **c.** $(3, -2, -2)$, $(9, -1, -1)$
d. $(5, 0, 1)$, $(-3, 0, 2)$ **5. a.** $x = -4 + 5s - 4t$
$y = -6 + 2s - 6t, \ z = 3 + 3s + 3t$
b. $x = 3t, y = 2s, z = 1$ **c.** $x = s, y = 0, z = t$
6. a. $\vec{r} = (-4, -1, 3) + s(1, 3, 4) + t(3, -4, -1)$
b. $\vec{r} = (0, 4, 0) + s(7, 0, 0) + t(0, 0, -2)$
c. $\vec{r} = s(1, 0, 0) + t(0, 0, 1)$

7. a. $\vec{r} = (-4, 5, 1) + s(-3, -5, 3) + t(2, -1, -5)$
b. $\vec{r} = (4, 7, 3) + s(1, 4, 3) + t(-1, -1, 3)$
c. $\vec{r} = (8, 3, 5) + s(5, 2, -3) + t(11, -1, -1)$
d. $\vec{r} = (0, 1, 3) + s(2, 1, -2) + t(4, -4, 7)$
e. $\vec{r} = (2, 6, -5) + s(5, 5, -1) + t(4, -8, 7)$
8. a. $x = 7 + 4s - 3t, y = -5 - s + 4t, \ z = 2 + s + 4t$
b. $x = 5 + 2s + 4t, y = 4 - 2t, z = 2 - 9s + t$
c. $x = 8 + 5s + 2t, y = 3 - 2s + 2t, z = 5 + 11s - 5t$
d. $x = 3 + s + 3t, y = 2 - 2s - 2t, z = 2 + 4s + 2t$
e. $x = 2 + 5s + 4t, y = 6 + 5s - 8t, z = -5 - s + 7t$
9. a. $\vec{r} = (6, 4, 2) + s(0, 1, 0) + t(0, 0, 1)$
b. $\vec{r} = s(1, 1, 1) + t(8, -1, -1)$ **c.** $\vec{r} = s(1, 0, 0) + t(1, 4, 7)$
10. a. the three points are collinear **b.** the point is on the line
11. $\vec{r} = (7, 0, -7) + s(0, 0, 1) + t(1, 2, -1)$; $x = 7 + t, y = 2t,$
$z = -7 + s - t$ **13. b.** All points in and on the parallelogram
whose vertices have position vectors $\vec{a}, \vec{b}, -\vec{a} + \vec{b} + \vec{c}$ and $\vec{c}$
14. b. all points on and between the parallel lines

Exercise 4.2

1. a. $7x + y - z - 18 = 0$ **b.** $x - 5 = 0$ **c.** $2x + 3z + 6 = 0$
d. $2x - y + 4z = 0$ **2. a.** $y + 2 = 0$ **b.** $z - 3 = 0$
c. $x - y - 2z + 3 = 0$ **3. a.** $Ax + By + Cz = 0$ **b.** $D = 0$
5. a. $12x + 8y + 13z = 0$ **b.** $3x - 8y + z - 15 = 0$ **c.** $x - 2 = 0$
d. $3x + 10y - 4z + 4 = 0$ **e.** $x - 2 = 0$
f. $12x + 8y + 13z = 0$; a and f, c and e are coincident
6. a. $4x - 13y - 20z + 30 = 0$ **b.** $9x - 6y - 2z + 22 = 0$
7. a. $11x + 8y - 2z - 21 = 0$ **b.** $x + 3y + z = 0$ **c.** $y - 1 = 0$
d. $6x - 2y + 5z = 0$ **8.** $y + 2z = 0$
9. $10x + 11y - 10z - 50 = 0$ **10. a.** parallel and distinct
b. neither **c.** coincident **d.** coincident
11. a. $\vec{r} = (0, -24, 0) + s(1, 2, 0) + t(0, 3, 1)$
b. $\vec{r} = (0, 0, 3) + s(5, 0, 3) + t(0, 1, 0)$
12. a. parallel to and on the plane **b.** parallel to the plane, not on
c. not parallel **13. a.** $17°$ **b.** $90°$ **15. a.** $6x - 4y - 4z - 3 = 0$
b. a plane passing through the mid point of AB and having normal
$\overrightarrow{AB}$. **16. b.** $38x + 33y + 111z - 103 = 0$
17. $x = 3t, y = -2t, z = 0$ **18.** $|D|$ will be the distance
from the origin to the plane **20.** $\dfrac{x}{a} + \dfrac{y}{b} + \dfrac{z}{c} = 1$

Exercise 4.3

1. a. $(4, 6, -2)$ **b.** $(1, 1, 2)$ **c.** no intersection
d. $(x, y, z) = (2 - t, 14 - t, 1 + t)$ **e.** $(5, 15, -5)$
2. a. yes **b.** no **3. a.** $(2, 0, 0)$ **b.** $(0, -3, 0)$ **c.** $\left(0, 0, \dfrac{-6}{7}\right)$
4. a. (i) $\left(\dfrac{28}{27}, 0, 0\right)$ (ii) $\left(0, \dfrac{56}{55}, 0\right)$ (iii) $\left(0, 0, \dfrac{-7}{2}\right)$
b. (i) $\vec{r} = (-1, 2, 0) + k(-55, 54, 0)$
(ii) $\vec{r} = (0, 8, 24) + p(0, 16, 55)$
(iii) $\vec{r} = (4, 0, 10) + u(8, 0, 27)$ **5. a.** $(9, 14, 0)$
b. $\left(\dfrac{-3}{2}, 0, \dfrac{7}{2}\right)$ **c.** $(0, 2, 3)$ **6. a.** one point **b.** infinite number
of points **c.** no points, one point, or an infinite number of points
7. $\left(\dfrac{3}{2}, -1, \dfrac{7}{2}\right)$ **8.** $\left(\dfrac{14}{5}, \dfrac{-2}{5}, -6\right)$ **9. a.** 1, 4, 3 **b.** 5, $\dfrac{-5}{2}$, -5
c. -4, 8, -8 **d.** 4, -16, 8 **10. a.** x-intercept is 4,
y-intercept is 4; intersection with: xy plane is
$\vec{r} = (u, 4 - u, 0)$, xz plane is $\vec{r} = (4, 0, s)$,
yz plane is $\vec{r} = (0, 4, t)$ **b.** x-intercept is 3; intersection with:
xy plane is $\vec{r} = (4, t, 0)$, xz plane is $\vec{r} = (4, 0, u)$

c. y-intercept is $-\frac{1}{2}$; intersection with: xy plane is $\vec{r} = \left(t, \frac{-1}{2}, 0\right)$, yz plane is $\vec{r} = \left(0, \frac{-1}{2}, s\right)$

d. x-intercept is 2, z-intercept is 6; intersection with: xy plane is $\vec{r} = (2, t, 0)$, xz plane is $\vec{r} = (u, 0, 6 - 3u)$, yz plane is $\vec{r} = (0, s, 6)$

e. y-intercept is 0, z-intercept is 0; intersection with: xy and xz plane is $\vec{r} = (t, 0, 0)$, yz plane is $\vec{r} = (0, 2u, u)$, **f.** x, y, is and z-intercepts are each 0; intersection with: xy plane is $\vec{r} = (t, -t, 0)$, xz plane is $\vec{r} = (s, 0, s)$, yz plane is $\vec{r} = (0, u, u)$

11. a. no value **b.** $k = 9$ **c.** $k \neq 9$

Exercise 4.4

2. a. yes **b.** no **c.** no **d.** yes **3. a.** $x = 7 + 5t$, $y = -3 - 2t$, $z = t$ **b.** parallel **c.** $x = 8 - 7t$, $y = t$, $z = 11 - 10t$

d. $x = 0$, $y = 1 - t$, $z = t$ **e.** parallel

4. a. $\begin{bmatrix} 3 & -7 & 1 & | & 12 \\ 1 & 1 & -2 & | & -3 \end{bmatrix}$ **b.** $\begin{bmatrix} -4 & 3 & 2 & | & 4 \\ 0 & 2 & -5 & | & 5 \end{bmatrix}$

c. $\begin{bmatrix} 1 & 0 & 4 & | & 16 \\ 0 & 1 & -8 & | & -2 \end{bmatrix}$ **d.** $\begin{bmatrix} 6 & 5 & -2 & | & 4 \\ -2 & 5 & 3 & | & -4 \end{bmatrix}$

5. a. $x + 4z = 9$, $y - 6z = 4$

b. $8x - 2y + 3z = -6$, $2x - 6y - 6z = 9$

c. $5x - 10y = 8$, $3y - 4z = 6$ **d.** $x + 4z = 0$, $y + 9z = 0$

6. a. $\vec{r} = (10, -3, 0) + t(-15, 4, 1)$

b. $\vec{r} = \left(\frac{5}{9}, \frac{-10}{9}, 0\right) + t(-3, 0, 1)$

c. $\vec{r} = \left(\frac{13}{4}, 0, \frac{1}{4}\right) + t(-4, 1, 0)$

d. $\vec{r} = (0, 0, -2) + t(2, 1, 0)$

e. $\vec{r} = (7, -8, 0) + t(0, 3, 1)$ **f.** $\vec{r} = (0, 0, -3) + t(1, 0, 2)$

7. a. 3 planes intersect at the point $\left(\frac{-253}{30}, \frac{106}{15}, \frac{154}{15}\right)$

b. no solution, the 3 lines are not concurrent **c.** the 4 planes have no common intersection

8. b. $4x + 5y - 14z = 0$ **c.** $8x - 8y - 12z + 15 = 0$

9. $x - z - 14 = 0$

Exercise 4.5

2. a. coplanar **b.** coplanar **c.** coplanar **d.** collinear

3. a. $\left(5\frac{1}{2}, 2, 3\right)$ **b.** $(0, 5, 0)$ **c.** $(-2, 1, 1, -3)$ **4.** $\left(\frac{47}{5}, \frac{-27}{5}, -5\right)$

5. a. $\begin{bmatrix} 3 & 1 & -5 & | & 12 \\ 1 & -5 & 2 & | & -3 \end{bmatrix}$ **b.** $\begin{bmatrix} 1 & 5 & 0 & | & 8 \\ 0 & 3 & 2 & | & -6 \end{bmatrix}$

$x = 8$, $y = -6$, $z = 3$ **c.** $\begin{bmatrix} 0 & 4 & -3 & | & 12 \\ 2 & 5 & 0 & | & 15 \\ 4 & 0 & 6 & | & 10 \end{bmatrix}$ **6. a.**

b. $x - 6z = 4$, $y + 5z = -5$, $0z = 0$ **c.** $x = 0$, $y = 0$, $0z = 1$

7. $\left(\frac{27}{4}, \frac{-15}{4}, \frac{-25}{4}\right)$ **8. a.** unique solution point $(x, y, z) = (2, 3, 4)$

b. no solution, 3 distinct parallel planes **c.** infinite number of solutions, the planes intersect in the line with equation $(x, y, z) = (7 - t, t, 2)$ **d.** Infinite number of solutions, the 3 planes are coincident, $x - 2y - 3z = 1$ **e.** no solution, 2 of the planes are parallel and distinct **f.** no solution, 2 planes are coincident, and the third is parallel and distinct **g.** infinite number of solutions intersecting in the line $(x, y, z) = (6 + t, -1 - t, 2t)$ **h.** no solution, planes form a triangular prism **i.** unique solution, the origin $(0, 0, 0)$ **9.** $\frac{-7}{19}$

Review Exercise

2. a. $\vec{r} = (-1, -1, 2) + s(5, 4, 2) + t(0, 0, 1)$; $x = -1 + 5s$, $y = -1 + 4s$, $z = 2 + 2s + t$

b. $\vec{r} = (1, 1, 0) + s(0, 1, 0) + t(3, 1, -3)$; $x = 1 + 3t$, $y = 1 + s + t$, $z = -3t$

c. $\vec{r} = (0, 0, 4) + s(2, -3, 0) + t(1, 0, 2)$; $x = 2s + t$, $y = -3s$, $z = 4 + 2t$

d. $\vec{r} = s(1, 1, 1) + t(3, 4, 5)$; $x = s + 3t$, $y = s + 4t$, $z = s + 5t$ **e.** $\vec{r} = (3, -1, 2) + s(4, 0, 1) + t(4, 0, 2)$ $x = 3 + 4s + 4t$, $y = -1$, $z = 2 + s + 2t$ **3. a.** $x + 3y + 5z - 67 = 0$

b. $2x - 3y - 11z + 33 = 0$ **c.** $y + z - 6 = 0$

d. $8x + 2y + z - 18 = 0$ **e.** $z - 7 = 0$ **f.** $x - 3y - 3 = 0$

4. a. $\frac{1}{3}$ **b.** $k = 5$ or $k = -4$ **5.** $7x + 2y - 4z - 13 = 0$
6. $\vec{r} = s(1, 2, -1) + t(2, -3, 2)$ **7.** $2x - y = 0$
8. $x - 3y + 2z - 14 = 0$ **9.** $17x - 7y + 13z - 23 = 0$

11. a. $\frac{54}{\sqrt{37}}$ **b.** $\frac{4}{\sqrt{14}}$ **c.** $\frac{2}{\sqrt{5}}$ **d.** $\frac{3}{2\sqrt{30}}$ **12.** $\frac{22}{7}$ **13.** $\left(\frac{4}{5}, \frac{-2}{5}, 1\right)$

14. $(-5, 0, 0)$, $(0, -4, 0)$, $(0, 0, 20)$ **17. a.** $k \neq \frac{9}{2}$

b. will never intersect in a line **c.** $k = \frac{9}{2}$

18. a. $3x + 4y - z - 1 = 0$ **b.** $\vec{r} = (0, 3, 3) + t(3, 4, -1)$

c. $\left(\frac{-12}{13}, \frac{23}{13}, \frac{43}{13}\right)$ **19.** $27x + 11y + 7z - 53 = 0$

20. a. $4x - y + z = 0$ **21.** coincident **22. a.** in $R^2 - 2$ lines intersect in the point $\left(\frac{1}{2}, \frac{3}{2}\right)$, in $R^3 - 2$ planes intersecting in the line $\vec{r} = \left(\frac{1}{2}, \frac{3}{2}, t\right)$ **b.** no solution, 2 parallel planes

c. line $\vec{r} = (-1, 1, 0) + t(6, 5, 7)$ **d.** point $(2, 3, -1)$

e. no solution, triangular prism

f. line $\vec{r} = (5, 1, 0) + t(-3, 0, 1)$

g. line $\vec{r} = (1, -2, 0) + t(-1, 3, -5)$

h. planes coincident with $x - z = 4$ **i.** no solution, 2 planes are parallel and distinct

Chapter 4 Test

1. a. planes are perpendicular and intersect in a line **b.** planes are parallel **c.** planes are parallel **2. a.** line is parallel to the plane, no solution **b.** intersects the plane at $(2, 2, 0)$ **4. a.** $(-5, 0, 0)$

b. $\vec{r} = (0, 0, 5) + t(1, 0, 1)$ **5.** $4x - 4y + 7z = 0$

6. planes intersect in a line with equation $\vec{r} = (0, 1, -5) + t(1, -3, 5)$

7. a. $\sqrt{14}$ **b.** $\frac{54}{\sqrt{14}}$ **c.** opposite side

Cumulative Review Chapters 1–4

3. 0 **4. b.** $(-5, 5, 5)$ **5.** yes **6.** $2x - 3y - 3z - 12 = 0$

7. $A\left(\frac{7}{11}, \frac{4}{11}, 3\right)$, $B\left(\frac{3}{11}, \frac{6}{11}, \frac{27}{11}\right)$ **8.** $x + 2y + 2z - 20 = 0$

9. a. no intersection **b.** $\vec{r} = (-1, 3, 0) + t(1, 2, -1)$ **c.** $\left(\frac{-5}{2}, 0, \frac{3}{2}\right)$

10. $\left(2, \frac{1}{2}, 0\right)$ **11.** $\left(2, \frac{5}{2}, \frac{5}{2}\right)$ **12. a.** $x = -1 - t$, $y = 3 + t$, $z = t$

b. xy plane at $(-1, 3, 0)$, xz plane at $(2, 0, -3)$, yz plane at $(0, 2, -1)$ **c.** $3\sqrt{3}$ **13.** $\left(\frac{103}{11}, \frac{-93}{11}, \frac{60}{11}\right)$

14. $(24, 36, 8)$ **15.** $\pm \frac{3}{2\sqrt{109}}$ **16.** $a = \frac{1}{2}b$, $b \neq -2$

17. $(x, y, z) = (3, -1, 0)$ **18. a. (i)** $k = 2$ **(ii)** $k \neq 2$, $k \neq -1$ **(iii)** $k = -1$ **b.** planes intersect in the line $(x, y, z) = (t, t, t)$.

Index